NIGHT BOMBER 3

DEPTH CHARGE DANGER 101

ISLAND OF FEAR 201

NIGHT BOMBER

THE V-2 THREAT

In 1937, two years before World War II officially began, a new weapons research establishment was set up by Hitler's Nazi Government in the tiny fishing village of Peenemunde on the northern coast of Germany on the Baltic. Here scientists and weapons experts were gathered with one specific instruction: to develop a liquid-fuelled rocket capable of carrying a high-explosive warhead to be used in military bombardments. Their instructions were to produce a rocket capable of carrying one ton of explosives a distance of 160 miles.

At the outbreak of war in 1939, anonymous information was passed to the British about the work being carried out at this secret weapons research establishment, but at that time it was dismissed as false propaganda spread by the Germans in order to frighten Britain; however, in December 1942 more concrete evidence was gained by British intelligence. Reconnaissance flights by the RAF over the area confirmed these intelligence reports.

The British War Cabinet realized that if the weapons being developed – now known to be the V-2 rockets – were launched against Britain then whole cities could be devastated without any defence.

Unless Peenemunde could be destroyed, then the War would be lost.

Our story begins in the summer of 1943.

On Fire!

Until you've been inside an aeroplane that's on fire there is no way you can imagine how it feels. The heat, the flames, doing your best to fight the rising panic, knowing that there is no way out except jumping out at 12,000 feet and hoping your parachute opens. In my case that wasn't an option, the tracer from the German fighters had torn through the skin of our fuselage and peppered my 'chute, ripping it to shreds.

"What's the news, John?!" came the voice of Danny Roberts, our Captain, over my headphones.

"Our tail's on fire, skipper!" I reported back. "Looks like the rear turret's gone. Can't see Ian yet…"

Ian was our rear gunner. I was John Smith, 19 years old, flight engineer, and this was my seventh mission on a Lancaster bomber. Lucky seven, they say. Not for us.

We'd been coming back from a bombing raid on a German industrial town. Our bombs had hit the target and we were on our return flight, heading for our base in Lincolnshire. As we left the Dutch coast, heading over the North Sea, we relaxed. We'd made it, or so we thought. And then suddenly, halfway across the sea, German fighters were on us. Focke-Wulfs, Stukas, Messerschmitts, the air filled with fighter planes hurtling past us on either side, flying below us, above us, and each of them hammering tracer into us. Our gunners did their best to return fire and cut them down, but there were just too many of them.

I'd been sitting in my seat next to Danny when the shout had come from Ian in the rear turret. "We're on fire here!"

"See if you can put it out, John," ordered Danny.

I'd grabbed a fire extinguisher and headed for the rear of the plane. It was as I did this that a tracer of bullets from one of the fighters came through the plane and tore my parachute to bits.

As I scrambled along the narrow passageway from the front of the plane towards the rear, clambering over wing spars and squeezing past machinery, above me I could hear the chatter chatter chatter of the guns in the dorsal turret. Through all this noise I could just about make out the voice of Malcolm, our radio operator, shouting into his radio set, trying to raise help.

I reached the rear of the plane, but the air was thick with smoke and my eyes began to water from the acrid fumes. I realized what had happened. The German fighter's bullets had burst the hydraulic pipes that operated the turret and the guns, and oil was pouring out.

Suddenly there was the sound of rapid shooting from the turret. The ammunition had begun to explode.

There was no sign of Ian, just a raging inferno of flames, forcing me back.

I pulled the handle of the extinguisher and began to shoot foam into the flames, trying to identify the seat of the fire, but as fast as I dampened down one part another sprang up.

Suddenly an explosion from the front of the Lancaster echoed all the way along the plane and rocked me off my feet, throwing me backwards. I could feel the plane going into a dive, then we pulled out abruptly.

"Outer starboard engine gone!" came Danny's voice over our headsets. "Inner starboard engine on fire! John, I need you back up here!"

"Coming, skipper!" I called back. "The rear's still blazing!"

"OK, John, leave it to me! I'll do it!" came Malcolm's voice. "I'm on my way to join you, skipper!"

I worked the extinguisher, trying to douse the flames, now blinded by the smoke.

"English coast ahead!" shouted Tommy, then his voice went suddenly dead. I didn't know whether it was because of an electrical fault, or whether the fire at the front had suddenly engulfed the cockpit and then back to the navigator's position. All I knew was the flames here in the rear turret were starting to die down. The air was still thick with smoke and fumes from smouldering pieces of equipment, but it seemed to be under some sort of control.

As I turned to head back along the narrow passageway, the front of the plane suddenly dived and I was hurled upwards and backwards, into the smouldering remains of the turret.

The huge plane hurtled down down down. Over my headphones I could hear a voice screaming, but I couldn't work out whose it was. I struggled to regain my balance, clawing my way downwards towards the passageway. The plane gave another lurch, and then momentarily straightened up, and I found myself sliding forwards, slipping in oil.

I struggled back to my feet.

Radio contact was now completely down and I could hear nothing. I saw a cloud of thick smoke pouring at me from down the narrow passageway, and then the plane went into another drastic dive ... down down down down...

I managed to grab a handhold on one of the metal spars ... and suddenly I felt myself snatched away, my feet left the floor and I was flying through the air... Then there was a tremendous CRACK! as my head hit something hard, and then there was nothing...

Recovery

Waking up was like slowly emerging from deep underwater. I broke through the surface and when I opened my eyes there was a sort of mist over them. There was a face in front of me, looking down, the most beautiful face I'd ever seen. Her skin was fair with her red hair forming a halo around her head. Her eyes were a soft green. Everything else was white. It suddenly struck me that I was dead, and before I could stop myself I blurted out: "Are you an angel?"

"No, just a junior nurse," she said, and she smiled.

I became aware of the noise, the clanking of trolleys, the hustle and bustle of people. I blinked my eyes to try and focus them, and turned my head to look around. It hurt my neck to move it, and I so brought my head back to look at the nurse again. She still looked as beautiful as before, but now everything else was in focus. I was in a hospital. "How do you feel?" she asked.

"I don't know," I said.

I remembered the plane going down…

"Are the others OK?" I asked. "The chaps who were in the plane with me?"

A look of sadness crossed her face, clouding her green eyes, and I knew that something terrible had happened.

"They're badly injured, aren't they?" I said.

She hesitated, and just then a man in a white coat appeared beside her.

"So, our young patient is awake at last," he said.

The nurse turned to him.

"He … he was asking about the rest of his crew."

The doctor nodded.

"Thank you, Nurse Evans," he said. "I'll deal with this from here."

Nurse Evans gave me a last look, forced a smile, then went off about her duties.

"You were very lucky, young man," said the doctor. "They found you some distance from the wreckage. You must have been thrown clear just before it crashed."

"The others," I insisted. "How are they? Where are they?"

The doctor took a breath.

"There's no good way to tell you, I'm afraid. They're dead."

For a second I was stunned.

"All of them? Danny? Andy? Malcolm…?"

The doctor nodded.

"All of them. Three died immediately on impact, the other three died later of their wounds. I'm sorry. It was a miracle you survived. You must have been unconscious when you were thrown clear of the plane."

"Yes, I was," I said, though my mind was still racing at the thought of the rest of my crew being dead. My pals, gone, just like that.

"It was lucky you were," continued the doctor. "Because of that you were limp when you were thrown out. Some bruising and cuts, that's all. If you'd been awake and tense, you would have broken something for sure." I didn't answer him, I just couldn't believe what had happened. The doctor nodded, aware of what was going through my mind. He must have had this same terrible task of breaking bad news hundreds of times.

"I'll let you rest," he said. "If you need anything, call a nurse. They'll look after you. But try not to call on them too much, if you can help it. They're run off their feet with the huge amount of patients we're trying to deal with."

I nodded, and he went.

I lay in that hospital bed and thought of them. Danny. Andy. Malcolm. Ben. Ian. Tommy. I thought of the good times we'd had together. The times in the mess. Andy with his jokes. Ian with his songs, sung in that terrible voice of his. I thought of us all, comrades together in our Lancaster P Peter. The missions we'd flown. The near-misses we'd had. And the last one, the fire and smoke inside the plane. There'd be no more missions for us together.

They kept me in hospital for another three days. I don't think they'd have let me stay that long if they hadn't been worried that there might be something more serious wrong with me. I knew the bang I'd received on the head worried them and they were concerned I might suddenly black out or get delayed concussion. My wounds had been stitched up and the nurses told me they were healing nicely, although when I looked in the mirror I thought I looked like a junior version of Frankenstein's monster.

I discovered that I'd been unconscious for 24 hours. They'd found me lying on top of a haystack about four hundred yards from where the plane had crashed into a field. The Lancaster had still been engulfed in flames when the fire engines arrived. The others had been trapped inside, unable to get out. I'd been thrown clear out through the hole where the rear turret used to be, unconscious. I'd landed on the haystack and had just suffered bruising and lacerations. As the doctor said, it had been a miracle. If it had been me who'd gone to the front to fight the fire, instead of Malcolm… If he'd been standing by the rear turret instead of me…

But it hadn't. They'd died and I'd survived.

The only positive thing about being in the hospital was getting to know the nurse who'd been watching me when I came round. Nurse Evans. Susan. She was 19, the same age as me. It was strange, I'd always been tongue-tied around girls before, but with Susan it was different. When she had a moment between shifts she'd come and sit by my bed and we'd talk. And by the second day, when I was allowed up, we found time to go for walks in the hospital grounds, when her work allowed her.

She told me about her life growing up in Nottingham, and I told her about mine growing up in London.

I told her how I'd come to be in the RAF as a flight engineer.

"I was two years into an engineering apprenticeship when war broke out," I said. "I went along to the recruiting office and volunteered to continue doing my engineering, but for the RAF. Aircraft engineers were in very short supply, so they took me in. At first I started on smaller planes, but then the big bombers came in." I could feel myself smile as I thought about the first time I'd been put on to working on a large bomber. A Halifax. "There is no machine like it," I said. "It's so huge, so fragile, and so powerful, all at the same time. From there, it was on to Lancasters. They're the best of all."

As we walked along the hospital corridor, all around us were posters warning us that "Careless Talk Costs Lives". During my training I'd also been told time and time again that the stranger who we chatted to might well be a German spy. But the thought of Susan being a spy just made me laugh. I knew I could trust her.

"How long have you been actually flying?" she asked. "You know, on missions?"

"Three months," I said.

"And safe until this one," she asked.

I shook my head.

"No," I said. "This is the second time my crate's crashed."

She gave me a quizzical look.

"Were you badly injured?"

"Ribs," I nodded. "Plus a load of stitches. I'm getting to be a regular sewing cushion." I sighed. "Two of our crew were killed that time. The pilot and the bomb aimer. The others were injured much worse than I was." I sighed again. "I'm beginning to think I'm a regular Jonah. The one who survives unharmed whilst everyone else gets killed."

"I'm glad you survived," she said.

And she slipped her arm through mine. Even though my heart was heavy at the thought of my dead comrades, a little moment of happiness crept in and warmed it.

My New Crew

On the third day at the hospital I was discharged and sent to a new base at RAF Wickenby in Lincolnshire. I just managed to grab enough time with Susan to give her the address of my new base and get her to promise to write, and then I was off, with my bag packed and my transport ticket in my pocket.

I was lucky; I caught a lift on a transport lorry doing a round trip of the bases in Lincolnshire with supplies. As I travelled, in between chatting to the driver and his mate, I wondered what my new crew would be like.

When I'd joined my last two crews, it had all been very casual. A case of us all being put into one room and gradually sorting ourselves out, with a pilot linking up with an engineer here, adding a rear gunner who looked as if he might be the kind of chap you wouldn't mind spending an evening with over a pint, that sort of thing. In this way crews just sort of grew.

I'd soon learnt that it was important that a crew got on well together. If they didn't it was more than just disagreeable, it could be a matter of life and death. Flying a huge heavy bomber like the Lancaster had to be done with complete co-ordination. Bad feeling between members of a crew could jeopardize the flying of the plane, and lives of the rest of the crew.

When I reported to Wickenby, the Station Officer examined my papers for what seemed like ages, before saying:

"Flight engineer, eh?"

"Yes, sir."

"Right. I suggest you report to Flying Officer Bob Campbell. He's the Captain of S Sarah. His crew are short of a flight engineer."

"Flying Officer Campbell, sir. Right, sir. Where do I find Captain Campbell?"

"Either in the mess, or over at the hangar. He likes to keep an eye on his plane. A bit like a mother hen. Ask for S Sarah. The chap checking it over will be Captain Campbell."

"Right, sir."

I saluted, and then went to the mess and asked for Captain Campbell. He wasn't there, and someone else directed me towards the hangar.

It was a long walk, but after days of being cooped up in hospital it was good to be back among aeroplanes and healthy airmen again.

At the hangar I asked after either S Sarah, or Flying Officer Bob Campbell, and one of the ground staff pointed them both out to me.

A short, stocky man was standing beside the huge

Lancaster looking up at the underside of the fuselage and the open doors of the huge bomb bay.

"Flying Officer Campbell?" I enquired.

"That's me," he nodded, turning to greet me. "What can I do for you, son?"

Bob Campbell had an open honest face and a cheerful grin, the sort of welcoming smile that made you feel as if you'd known him for years. He had the tanned look of an outdoors man. I guessed he was about 28 years old. I recognized his accent straight away as Canadian. Canadians from the RCAF, The Royal Canadian Air Force, had volunteered in their thousands to fly in the War against Hitler. Some whole bomber squadrons of the RAF were crewed entirely by Canadians. Some had elected to join mixed crews. Captain Campbell was obviously one of them.

"Sergeant Smith J, flight engineer, reporting for duty, sir. I've been allocated to you."

Captain Campbell's grin became wider.

"Good," he said. "We're short of a flight engineer and I was just wondering where I could get us one, when up you pop. You met the rest of the crew yet?"

"No, sir," I replied. "I was told to report straight to you."

"Fine, then let's go find the rest of the fun band who keep this bird in the air and get you acquainted."

"Yes, sir," I said.

"And you can knock off the 'sir' business when we're not surrounded by the top brass," he said. "Call me skipper, or Bob. What's the J stand for?"

"John, sir … er, skipper," I said.

We found the other five members of the crew of S Sarah out on a patch of grass at the back of the huts playing a game of football. A tall man stood in the goal between two rolled-up coats, and the others were playing attack and defend, with two attacking the goal, and two defending it. As Bob and I approached them, the tall man blocked a sure-fire shot with some very neat hand-work.

"OK, guys, time out, or half-time, or whatever you call it when you take a break!" called Bob. "Come and meet our new crew member!"

One of the men picked up the ball, and the five of them trotted over towards us. I could tell by the expressions on their faces that they were keen to find out what their new crew-mate was like.

"This here's John Smith," said Bob. "He's our new flight engineer. Introducing this motley crew, from the left: that tall one with the moustache that looks like a pair of bicycle handlebars is Flight Sergeant Andrew Wilmot, our bomb aimer."

This was the man who'd been in goal.

"Pleased to meet you," beamed Andrew. Tall and thin,

he had a firm handshake. Like Bob he had an easy smile, with large teeth peeping out from beneath his enormous handlebar moustache.

I nodded back in greeting, as Bob continued:

"Mr Muscles here is Flight Sergeant Bruce Trotter, our rear gunner."

"Mr Muscles" was a very appropriate nickname. Where Andrew was tall and thin, Bruce was short but wide, and with muscular shoulders and arms. He also had a moustache, but a short one, the sort my dad always called "a toothbrush", because it looked like just the bristles of a toothbrush stuck under the nose.

"Next to him is Sergeant Steve Williams, our pet Aussie from somewhere in the Australian outback."

Steve, like Bob, had the tanned dark skin of a man who had spent a lot of time in the sun. However, he was insistent that sun wasn't in the outback.

"I come from Sydney, and Sydney is not the outback," objected Steve. "Sydney is a huge and growing city, and a lot more modern than most of the places in this country."

"Listen to the Colonials fight among themselves," grinned another tall man at the back.

"Less of that 'Colonials' stuff, George," said Bob, but with a good-humoured touch in his voice. "And this man who has just insulted your Captain is Sergeant George Brien."

"It wasn't an insult, skip," protested George. As tall as Andrew, at least six feet tall, George was noticeable because of his balding head. "In my opinion," George continued, "you blokes out in the Colonies are the best there is, coming back here and fighting for the old country. In fact I'm giving you praise."

"Which won't get you any promotion," said Bob. "And last but not least, our navigator, Sergeant Wally Bristow."

Wally nodded to me in friendly enough greeting, but I thought I detected a look of uncertainty in his face. Wally was a small man with a pale complexion and what looked like a permanent frown on his face. He was the only one who didn't greet me with a friendly grin.

"John Smith, eh?" he said.

"That's me," I said.

"And how come you're a flight engineer without a crew?" Wally asked, curious.

"Bad manners, Wally," commented Andrew. "Delving into another chap's history."

"I just like to know who I'm flying with," said Wally.

"It's no secret," I said. "I lost my last crew when the plane we were in came down and caught fire. The one before that, we lost a wing coming in over the coast. I was lucky both times." My voice dropped as I added: "I'm afraid most of the others weren't."

There was an awkward silence as this sunk in, and I realized it probably hadn't been a good idea to be quite so honest.

"Well, sounds to me like John's lucky," Steve said, trying to lighten the mood. "Anyone who survives twice like that is as good as a cat with nine lives."

"Anyone with that kind of luck is a jinx, if you ask me," scowled Wally. "He might walk away, but two crews lost? That's bad luck."

"Not everyone was killed," I defended, but I could feel that my words sounded hollow.

Bob Campbell came to my rescue.

"You can forget that kind of talk, Wally," said Bob sternly. "John's one of us, now, and that's that."

Turning to Steve, he said: "Right, Steve, take John along to the Stores and get him kitted out. We've got a war to win, and it won't be done hanging around here chewing the breeze!"

As I followed Steve towards the Stores I couldn't help but think about what Wally had said. It was the same worry I'd mentioned to Susan at the hospital. Was I really a Jonah? A jinx? Was I going to bring death to my new crew, the same way I'd brought it to my last two crews?

Into Combat

My chance to fly a combat mission with my new crew-mates came the very next day. In the late afternoon we had our briefing in which the officer gave us our targets: an industrial complex near the German city of Hamburg. We were to take off at 2300 hours.

That night, as I climbed on board the Lancaster with the rest of the crew, I couldn't help thinking of the last time I'd boarded a plane identical to this. Then I'd been smiling and joking with a different set of men: Danny, Andy, Malcolm, Ben, Ian, Tommy. All gone. Before that it had been another Lancaster with six other faces. Two of those had also died. This time I found it hard to put on a smiling face.

"Cheer up, John," grinned Steve as we climbed up the ladder. "You can only die once."

I forced a smile back at him, but over his shoulder I could see Wally's face glaring at me. I knew that this was a make-or-break flight for me. If this flight crashed and only I survived, I knew I'd never be able to set foot in another plane again. It was this feeling that I had to do well on this mission and do my best to get us back safely that helped me keep my fear of going back into combat under control. Because there was a sick feeling in my stomach as I took my seat on board and strapped myself in.

It wasn't too bad being the flight engineer of a Lancaster, it meant that you sat next to somebody – the pilot. The rest of the crew were in their own solitary stations and didn't see each other for the whole of the flight.

Bruce, our tail gunner, was all on his own in a turret at the rear of the plane. His only contact with anyone else was through the radio-telephone system, or R/T for short, in his helmet. The same went for Steve, our mid-upper gunner, who sat in a revolving turret right at the top of the plane, halfway along its fuselage.

Andrew, our bomb aimer, sat beneath my feet just in front of me in the forward turret. I couldn't see him because of the tangle of wires between us.

George, our radio operator, was stationed well behind my position, opposite the leading edge of the wing. It was George's job to keep his radio tuned in to our own Group frequency, as well as listen out for radio traffic between enemy fighters and their ground controls.

Wally, our navigator, was in his own little compartment behind Bob's seat. He was the only crew member who was allowed to have lights on so that he could check his maps and make sure we were on course, and so his compartment was curtained off. Only Bob and I at the front of the plane could actually see one another.

My job, as flight engineer, was to act as an assistant to the pilot when the plane took off. Once we were in the air, I had to look after the distribution of fuel to the different engines, and carry out repairs, if needed, to any of the systems. That is, if I could get to the parts that needed repairing. There isn't a lot of room to move about inside a Lancaster.

As was standard practice, Bob began by starting up the two inboard engines, the starboard one first. The procedure was always the same: outside, the ground starter battery was plugged in. In my role as "second pilot", I set the ground/flight switch to "ground", Bob set the throttle about half an inch open, the propeller switch was set fine, the slow-running switches off, the supercharger in M-gear, air intake control on cold, radiator shutters in automatic, the fuel selector cock on Number 2 tank.

With the ground crew operating the primer pump, I switched on the ignition and booster coil. Bob pressed the starter button.

There were a few preliminary bangs, then the Merlin engine picked up on the carburettor and fired.

We then went through the same procedure for the inboard port engine, and then the two outer engines.

Inside the plane the noise level began to increase. All

across the airfield I could see the other Lancasters going through the same procedure. By now all four of our engines were up and running. Bob ran the plane up against the wheel chocks to 1,500 rpm to check the eight magnetos, and then up to 3,000 rpm to check the boost.

He looked over to me, and I gave him a thumbs up. Everything seemed fine. We were ready to go.

One by one Bob checked with the crew in their positions over the R/T.

"Wally?"

"All OK, skip."

"George?"

"Fine."

And so on through us all.

The checks over, Bob signalled at the ground crew for them to remove the chocks that held our wheels in place. Then we were moving.

Bob rolled S Sarah forward and we joined the queue of Lancasters taxiing slowly towards the end of the runway, getting ready to be airborne.

I watched as the Lancaster ahead of us took to the skies, then it was our turn. We went through the last-minute checks: auto-pilot clutch in, DR compass set, elevator slightly forward, rudder neutral, aileron neutral. Then the standard fuel checks: crossfeeds off, booster pumps on Numbers 1 and 2 tanks, selector cocks on Number 2 tank. Then ready to go: superchargers set in M-gear, air intakes at cold, radiator shutters on automatic, flaps selected to 15 degrees down.

A green light from the control tower told us that we were clear for take-off. Bob let the brakes off and slowly opened the throttles. I could feel us swinging slightly to starboard, so I countered by leading with the starboard lever, putting us back on level course.

Bob and I, acting in unison, now opened the throttles wide and held them there. The engines were at plus-9 boost and at 3,000 rpm. Bob eased forward on the control column and we were off. As the airspeed indicator registered 100 mph, Bob began to apply backward pressure on the column. Suddenly we were airborne!

I put on the brakes for a second to stop the wheels from continuing to spin, and then retracted the undercarriage. Within seconds we were at 500 feet and travelling at 125 mph. Bob raised the flaps, pulled the throttle back to give us plus-6 boost at 2,850 rpm, and we began our climb. Up, up, up we went.

As we reached 16,000 feet the temperature changed dramatically. The Lancaster may have been 25 tons of wonderful fighting machine, but it was also as cold and draughty as an igloo with holes in the walls. There were two hot-air vents from the wing centre section, but most of this warm air went to the radio operator. The rest of us felt the ice-cold draughts coming in from tiny cracks in the front turret, the cockpit canopy and beneath us from the bomb bay.

We were all kitted out with electrically-heated suits which, in theory, should have kept us nice and cosy, but in practice it didn't work that way. With draughts, the icy cold outside, and the electrical circuits in the suits malfunctioning, every so often you stood a pretty good chance of either getting burns and blisters from your suit overheating, or frostbite from it cutting out altogether.

Now we were fully on our way I could feel myself starting to get nervous. Would we run into lots of flak? Would the German fighters be waiting for us? I took a deep breath to get hold of myself. It was always like this when we were on our way. I knew that once we were in the thick of battle the nerves would vanish. Then there would be just action. As my Training Officer had told me once, waiting to go into battle is often worse than actually fighting it.

Through the radio we were starting to get information from the windfinders at the front of the squadron about wind conditions. Wally, our navigator, made his adjustments to keep us on course and informed Bob over the R/T.

By now we were at 22,000 feet and flying at about 200 mph through the night sky. The noise from the Merlin engines filled the plane. Without our radio headsets we wouldn't have been able to hear one another, even if we'd just been a few inches apart. We'd been flying for almost three hours before we finally saw land.

"German coast five miles ahead," Wally warned.

"Roger," responded Bob. "Want to check your guns, fellas?"

"Roger that, skipper," came Steve's voice through my headphones.

Steve fired first, letting off a burst to clear his guns of any ice that might have formed. When he'd finished, Bruce did the same.

Wally let us know that we were about to cross the German coast.

"Got it," said Bob. "OK, Andrew, throw out the Window."

This "Window" was a new device. The boffins had come up with it some time ago, but it was only in the last few weeks that Bomber Command had actually been allowed to use it.

"Window" was the name given to thin strips of tinfoil, each one a foot long by half an inch wide. They were packed into bundles held together by brown paper. Andrew's job was to push them down a chute. As soon as the bundles hit the slipstream of the Lancaster, the paper burst open and the thin strips of tinfoil scattered and drifted towards the ground, completely disrupting enemy radar. All the Germans would see on their screens was a blizzard of dots and slashes, with no way to identify any planes coming in.

So far it had been a fairly quiet trip. My nerves we easing. I had even started to forget Wally's comment about my being a jinx. All that was about to change.

"Ten minutes to target," Wally informed us.

"Fighter coming in from the rear!" shouted Bruce suddenly.

I heard the chatter chatter chatter of Bruce's gun, then Steve in the mid-upper position, joined the action. Above it all I heard the whine of tracer from the incoming fighter. We were in trouble.

"Coming in from starboard!" shouted Bruce.

Bob immediately turned the Lancaster to port to miss the line of tracer from the German fighter, and then swung the heavy bomber back again. He began to weave the plane from side to side, desperately trying to avoid enemy fire. The sound of gunfire, both from outside the plane, and coming through my headphones, was deafening.

Suddenly there was an explosion on our starboard side that lit up the night sky.

"Got him!" roared Steve.

I let out a sigh of relief.

"Five minutes to target," reported Wally.

"Taking up position at the bombsight," responded Andrew.

I could hear Andrew's voice guiding Bob towards the target.

"Right ... steady ... right, right ... steady ... left ... right ... right a bit more ... OK."

Then we were over the target. There was a loud click as Andrew released the bombs.

"Bombs gone!" came Andrew's voice.

We all waited for the plane's usual surge upwards as the bomb load left, making us that much lighter, but it didn't happen.

"What's up, Andrew?!" called Bob. "Something wrong?"

"The mechanism's jammed!" shouted Andrew. "The bombs are stuck in the hold!"

Disaster!

When I heard Andrew's words a hollow feeling crept into the pit of my stomach. I knew what all the rest of the crew must be thinking. It was me, the jinx, bringing bad luck on them just as I'd brought bad luck on my last two crews.

"I'll check it, skipper," I said.

"My job," came Andrew's voice. "I'll do it!"

"I'm the engineer," I reminded him. "If it's a faulty mechanism I'll know what to do."

I said it with more confidence than I felt. All I knew was that I had to get those bombs unloaded. If I didn't their extra weight would mean we'd run out of fuel long before we got back to England. If we had to ditch in the sea with the weight of those bombs, we'd all drown for sure; the Lancaster would sink like a stone. And even if we did survive there was no way that anyone would find us in the sea at night.

I unstrapped myself and made my way down to the bomb bay.

I lifted the inspection covers above the bay. The doors were open and far far below me I could see the explosions as the other bombers hit the target, and the flak came up from the ground defences. The shapes of our large bombs were still securely stuck on their retainers. The hooks hadn't opened to release them.

I stretched my arms out to try to reach these hooks, but my fingers were just tantalizingly short.

"How you doing, John?" came Bob's voice in my earphones.

"Not good, skipper," I reported. "I'm going to have to chop away the floor and try to get to the hooks."

"Better be quick about it," said Bob. "The flak's getting worse, and their fighters are starting to get a bearing on us."

"We'll deal with them, skipper," came Bruce's voice. "Just get those bombs out of there, John."

I took the fire-axe from its mountings and began to chop away at the aluminium floor.

I could hear the rattle of our machine guns as both Bruce and Steve opened fire, doing their best to keep the attacking German fighters at bay.

Bullets from the enemy planes smacked into us, tearing holes in our fuselage.

"Faster would be good, John," said Bob urgently. "I'll make one last pass over the target area, but then I'm going to have to turn and head for home, fully loaded."

"Going as fast as I can, skipper!" I responded.

I heard someone approach behind me.

"Need any help, mate?" asked Andrew.

I nodded. By now I had made a large enough hole in the floor of the plane to get at the actual retaining hooks that held the bombs in place.

"I'm going to smash the hooks off with the axe," I said. "Can you hold my legs while I do it?"

"Got it," nodded Andrew.

I pushed myself forward through the hole until I was hanging over the open bomb bay. I felt Andrew get a hold on my legs and hoped that his grip was tight. The last thing I wanted was to plunge to the ground 20,000 feet below.

In this awkward position, I began hitting as hard as I could. Despite the freezing cold wind coming up at me, I was sweating like a pig. My arm ached terribly as I hacked and hacked at the hooks.

"Careful! Don't hit the bombs!" warned Andrew.

I was too tired to even reply. I took one last exhausted swing and the bombs dropped, taking one of the bomb doors with them. I lurched forward, nearly falling into the bomb bay. Luckily Andrew had a firm hold on my legs and he gripped them tightly.

Andrew pulled me back and I lay on the floor, panting.

"Bombs away, skipper!" I managed to gasp into my headset.

"Good job, and on target!" said Bob in relief. "Right, guys, we're heading home!"

Sedley

On our return to base there was a lot of talk about what had happened to our bombs. Why hadn't they left the plane when they should have?

As we headed for HQ and our debriefing Wally was the one who expressed his opinion openly to Bob.

"It's because he's a jinx," he said, pointing at me.

"Don't talk rubbish, Wally!" snorted Bob. "You surely don't believe in all that twaddle!"

"You mean you don't?" responded Wally. "In that case why do you wear a rabbit's foot on a piece of string around your neck?"

I looked at Bob in surprise. I suppose because I'd only recently joined the crew I hadn't noticed it.

"Because it's a family heirloom," replied Bob coolly. "It got my dad through 25 years in the police force, and if it was good enough for him, it's good enough for me."

It was obviously a lie, but it brought a smile to the faces of the rest of the crew.

I felt uncomfortable with the whole conversation and so didn't respond. I had to admit that if I'd been Wally, I might have felt the same way. What had gone wrong to make the bomb mechanism jam that way?

"If you ask me, John's a hero," said Andrew. "I saw him hack away at those bombs and free them, hanging there over the open bomb bay. If it hadn't been for him, we'd all be dead for sure right now. Or flying on empty tanks trying to grow wings."

"If it hadn't been for him we wouldn't have been in that situation in the first place," insisted Wally. "I tell you, he's a jinx. We ought to get ourselves a new flight engineer. A lucky one."

"Oh yeah, like the last two we had?" said Bruce sarcastically.

At this I pricked up my ears, curious. I knew that they'd lost their last flight engineer, but I didn't know the details.

"One gets himself shot on a mission and the other runs away and pretends to have a breakdown."

"He didn't pretend, Bruce," said Bob calmly, always the one to see the other man's point of view. "Not everyone's up to doing this kind of thing. Ted just couldn't hack it, that's all. If you ask me, I think we're lucky to have a guy with us who can think and act quickly as John did just now. I say he stays with us."

There were nods from Steve and Andrew, but reserved silences from both Wally and George. I knew they weren't convinced.

"I still say he's a jinx," muttered Wally.

"Of course you do," grinned Bob. "But I suggest you keep your opinion to yourself until we get the engineer's report and find out what really caused those bombs to get stuck."

At our debriefing session the problem with the bomb mechanism was barely touched on. Our questioners were more interested in details about the target, and the German defences. The questions were endless.

"How much flak did you encounter? Was it heavy or light?"

"Did you meet much fighter activity?"

"Did you bomb the correct target indicators dropped by the Pathfinders?"

"Did your camera take accurate photos of the target after the bombing?"

"Did you see any of our bombers in trouble? Were any damaged? Did you see parachutes coming from them?"

It was hard going, but I knew that by putting together all our answers, the theory was the top brass would be able to work out if the operation had been successful, and what lessons could be learnt from it for future raids.

As we left the session, I couldn't stop thinking about the bomb mechanism. Had we been lucky? Or was it, as Wally had said, my bad luck that had caused the problem in the first place?

Later that day the armament officer's report on the bomb

mechanism came through. I had been on tenterhooks waiting for it worried that it might say that I, as flight engineer, had made some sort of mistake. Instead the reason was very simple – terrifyingly so. The undersides of all Lancaster bombers were sprayed with matt black paint to help them avoid being spotted at night by ground defences. The underside of our plane had recently been re-sprayed to cover damage it had taken. The black paint had got on to one of the ball bearings in the mechanism that operated the bomb releases and glued the bearing into its socket. When the bomb doors opened this ball bearing was supposed to leave its socket. In this way the electrical bombing circuit would be completed and the retaining hooks would release their grip on the bombs. In this particular case, this one small metal ball had remained stuck, and so the mechanism couldn't operate.

"See?" said Bob to the crew when we got the report. "The one who's at fault here is the idiot who painted the plane, not John."

I left the hangar with Bruce and we headed across the airfield towards the mess.

"One ball bearing!" I said, shaking my head at the incredible fact. "So small, and it could have killed the lot of us."

"That's the way it is," shrugged Bruce. "You never know when it's coming, or how."

Even though I was relieved it hadn't been my fault, I

couldn't shake off the nagging doubt that maybe my bad luck had made it happen to us in the first place.

Because I was thinking about this, as we walked across the grass, I didn't see another young airman heading towards me, and I bumped into him.

"Sorry," I apologized, and walked on.

"Well well," he sneered. "It's the jinx!"

I decided to ignore him. I carried on walking, but then I heard his voice snap, sharper this time.

"You! Jinx! Didn't you hear me?"

I turned and was about to respond with a sharp retort, but Bruce stopped me. "Stow it, Sedley," he snapped.

"So?" said the young man. "Big brother's here to look after the little baby."

"No one looks after me," I replied, angrily.

"Ease off, the pair of you," said Bruce. "Or are you going to fight in public and get yourselves court-martialled?"

"I'll fight the jinx any time and any place he likes," said Sedley. "That is, unless you're scared."

"Why should I be scared of you?" I demanded.

"Any man who leaves his pals to burn like that so he can get out and survive has got to be scared."

This was too much! Before I knew it I'd taken a step towards Sedley, my fists clenched ready to let him have it, but Bruce stepped in and stopped me.

"Leave it, John," he said sharply. Turning to Sedley, he added warningly, "And if I hear of you interfering with John, you'll have me to deal with. And I fight like you Sedley, dirty."

Bruce grabbed me by the elbow and forced me away from the young airman, marching me towards the mess.

"Who is he?" I asked. "And why did he pick on me?"

"Because he's run out of other people to pick on," said Bruce. "His name's Terry Sedley, a bomb aimer with T Tommy. He's a nasty piece of work, and no mistake. Don't get in a fight with him, if you can avoid it. He's had two or three scraps since I've been here and each time he's really hurt the other poor bloke."

"Why hasn't he been arrested and charged?" I asked.

"Because every time it happens he claims he was defending himself against being attacked," explained Bruce. "And he's clever. He made sure there were witnesses around who had to swear the other guy had thrown the first punch."

"Like I nearly did back there," I said ruefully.

"Right," nodded Bruce. "And now he's got it in for you. So watch your step. And don't let him provoke you into anything. Because, believe me, you'll come off worst."

Shot To Pieces

It took the ground crew two days to patch up our damaged Lancaster. They cannibalized it with parts taken from other Lancs that were in sick bay. After two days of hanging around, waiting for action, we were ready to fly again. This time I took special care to inspect the paint spray-job to make sure no more ball bearings were gummed into their places with paint.

Over the next two weeks we flew seven more missions, five of them over Germany, and two to bomb an industrial complex in Milan, Italy.

Fortunately for me, there were no more accidents on these missions, and I was able to avoid any more mutterings from Wally about me being a jinx.

Meanwhile, Sedley's campaign against me continued. As Bruce had warned me, he was being very clever. He'd started a whispering campaign against me. The story he was telling was that I wasn't just a jinx, I was a coward who left his pals to die to save his own skin. He whispered in the mess that when he'd challenged me about this – "after all, someone's got to speak up for those poor chaps that coward Smith left to die" – I'd just walked away, afraid to face him.

I knew that he was trying to get me to challenge him, strike the first blow.

"Just let him talk," Bob advised me. "Words can't hurt you. And most of the guys know the sort of character you really are. The thing is, don't let Sedley drag you into anything."

"Just let him continue spreading his filthy lies about me?" I said bitterly.

"If you like I'll have a word with him," said Bob. "Or with some of the other guys he's talked to."

I shook my head.

"That'll just back up what he's saying," I said. "That I'm not man enough to stand up for myself and have to get my Captain to do it for me."

The one thing that kept my spirits up during this first couple of weeks on the base were the letters from Susan. Just like her, they were bright, witty, and they brought a ray of sunshine into my life.

Our next mission sent us back to bomb the heartland of the German industrial area in the Ruhr. This would be my sixteenth mission, which meant that if I came back from this, I would be over halfway through my first tour of duty.

The Ruhr was the armament and munitions centre of Germany. Naturally, it was heavily defended. Our problems were made worse on this raid because of the weather. The winds were much stronger than usual, and every now and then there was a clap of thunder and a streak of lightning.

As our bomber stream flew towards the target, the ground defences opened up. The searchlights lit up the sky with their beams, trying to pick us out. If they could catch us in a cone, a triangle of searchlights crossing at the same point, then there was usually no way to escape their ack-ack gunners.

I saw the Lancaster directly ahead of us suddenly caught in such a cone. Frantically the pilot tried to pull away, veering to port, desperate to get out of the probing searchlights, but it was no use. Burst after burst of fire from the ground defences tore into it, and we saw fire begin to spread along its wings. As I watched, the hatches opened and a few seconds later two parachutes opened. Then a third. They drifted downwards, heading towards the ground and certain capture. I held my breath, willing more parachutes to appear, but none did. The next second the crippled Lancaster exploded into a ball of flame and dropped out of the sky, spiralling down in smoke and flames. Four men dead.

There was no time to think about the loss, though, we had our own problems to contend with: the storm we had run into was now getting worse. The thunder crashed all around us, and the streaks of lightning ran along the length of the plane. Sheets of ice were also beginning to form along our wings.

Sitting next to Bob, I could see he was struggling with the controls as the ice took effect on the wing flaps.

"I'm going to have to fly lower. We have to get some of this ice off," he announced.

"You mean let the Germans shoot it off?" joked Bruce.

"Very funny," said Bob. "OK, everyone, get ready. It could be a bumpy ride from here."

Bob eased the controls forward and the huge Lancaster began to descend. As we went lower, the ground defences opened up at us. Flak burst all around us, shrapnel crashing into the plane and tearing holes in the aluminium fuselage.

"We'll never survive down here, skipper!" came Steve's voice. "The German fighters are coming for us like sharks on a swimmer!"

We were in a no-win situation. If we stayed up high, then we were in the eye of an ice storm, with the additional hazards of being hit by lightning. If we dropped below the storm to throw off the ice, then we were within easier reach of the German fighters, and also made a much better target for their ground defences.

Throughout the plane I could hear the metallic stuttering noise from Bruce and Steve's guns as they fired off bursts at the attacking fighters. Every now and then one of the fighters dodged the stream of bullets long enough to let off a burst of tracer that tore through the skin of our plane.

More and more holes were appearing in our fuselage.

"We're getting shot to pieces down here, skipper," I remarked.

"Every hole makes us that much lighter," cracked Bob. "How far are we from the target?"

"Five miles," came Wally's voice through our headphones.

"OK, then let's do it and go," said Bob. "Co-ordinates?"

Wally gave Bob the co-ordinates, and Bob turned the plane to make our bombing run. We'd left behind most of the others in our bombing stream, and we could see their tail lights making for home.

All around us fighters were letting off tracer at us. The night sky was filled with explosions from the flak.

"OK, you're on course, skipper," said Wally. "Three miles and closing. Two. One."

"Left a bit..." came Andrew's voice as he took over as bomb aimer. "Steady now... Bomb doors open."

The plane gave a lurch upwards.

"Bombs gone! OK, skipper, you can take us home!"

Decision Time

When we got back to base and were able to take a proper look at S Sarah, we were astonished. The fuselage was riddled with holes. Some near the tailplane were so big you could put both fists through them. It was a miracle that we'd got back home safely.

After our debriefing session, we heard that the plane would be grounded for at least 36 hours while the ground crew worked to repair it.

"Which gives us a breather," said Bob. "I've just been told that we've all got 24 hour leave, starting from 3 o'clock this afternoon, while they get the old girl back in shape. So, take it while it's here!"

The rest of the crew needed no further urging. Steve, Bruce and Wally headed off for London straight away. Andrew took the opportunity to go off and see his parents. George, the only married man amongst us, headed for Leeds to see his wife and children. Bob announced his intention to just stay at the base and get some well-earned rest.

As for me, as I watched my crew-mates head off for their leave, I couldn't shake off the feeling that Wally was right: I was a jinx. There was now no doubt in my mind that my bad luck had caused S Sarah to get shot up this badly. My two earlier planes had been wrecked and my mates killed. Now, twice since I'd joined them, the crew of S Sarah had been close to death.

I wondered whether I oughtn't to think about quitting. Maybe transferring to a ground crew. My bad luck might still follow me, but at least it wouldn't put six brave men at risk of their lives in the middle of the sky.

I needed to talk to someone about it. Susan.

It took me a long time to get to Nottingham. By the time I actually got to the hospital where she worked, half my leave had gone.

"Yes?" asked the receptionist.

"My name's Sergeant John Smith," I announced. "I'm here to see Nurse Susan Evans."

"I'm afraid she's not here," said the receptionist. "She's off duty for 24 hours. She's gone to see her parents. She's due back tomorrow."

My heart sank. All this way for nothing.

"What time?" I asked hopefully.

"Let me see…" The receptionist thumbed through the Duty Rotas. "She's due back at three o'clock tomorrow afternoon."

"But I'm due back at my base by then," I told her. "Can you give me her parents' address?"

The nurse shook her head.

"Sorry," she said. "We're not allowed to give out that sort of information."

Defeated, and feeling even worse than I had before, I left.

I spent a miserable night in Nottingham. I spent the evening in a pub, sitting mournfully at a table on my own with a pint of beer. Not even the singing that started up could cheer me up.

I found a bed for the night in a room over the pub, which I shared with a soldier who was also on leave, who kept me awake with drunken singing. When he did fall asleep he snored as loudly as the engine of a Lancaster. It was worse than being back at base.

The next morning I went back to the hospital and hung around in case Susan decided to come back on duty early, but I was as out of luck there as I had been the night before.

I managed to get a lift from a transport lorry heading back towards Lincolnshire. As I sat beside the driver and watched the road roll past, I reached a decision. As soon as I got back to base, I would quit. I'd tell Bob that I was putting in for a transfer to a ground crew.

Fight!

As I walked through the gates when I got back to base, Bob Campbell was the first one I saw.

"John!" he called.

"Hi, skipper!" I responded.

No time like the present, I thought. I took a deep breath and steeled myself to tell him that I was quitting his crew.

"Skipper, I've got something to tell you," I began.

"Tell me later, John," Bob cut me off. "I'm just rounding up the rest of the guys. There's a briefing in half an hour in the ops room. All crews. The word is that something big's in the offing. Really big. Dump your stuff in quarters and get over there. And don't hang about."

With that he hurried off.

OK, I thought. I'll tell him after the briefing.

I was about to head for my quarters, when I heard a voice sneer behind me, "So, the jinx has returned, has he?" My heart sank.

I turned. Sedley was there, with one of his cronies, Wilson.

"You're wasting your time, Sedley," I said, doing my best to remain looking cool and calm. "You're not going to provoke me. Go and have your fun with some other poor fool."

With that I turned and was about to walk off, when Sedley shouted after me: "You're a coward, Smith! A coward, and everyone knows it!"

I should have walked away from him there and then, but suddenly all the doubt and unhappiness that had been building up inside me suddenly seemed to boil over, and before I fully realized what I was doing I leapt at him, wanting to shut his mouth. It was what he had been waiting for. He knew I would go for him and he stepped nimbly aside. As I stumbled past him he tripped me and I went down heavily. I felt a tremendous pain in my side as his boot cracked into my ribs.

"Get him, Sedley!" shouted Wilson.

I felt rather than saw his boot coming at me again, and managed to roll clear just in time. The force of his kick not connecting unbalanced Sedley, and this gave me time to scramble to my feet. My ribs hurt and I wondered if any of them were broken.

Sedley came at me like a tiger, face contorted, and I jumped back. As I did so I thudded into a high stack of crates.

"Look out!" called Wilson.

Sedley and I both looked up. A crate had toppled off the top of the pile. Sedley turned to run, but he had no chance. The crate crashed down on top of him and he fell to the floor under it, out cold.

Wilson gaped down at his fallen pal, and then he looked at me. Fear was in his eyes.

"You really are a jinx!" he blurted out.

"What on earth is going on here?!" demanded an angry voice.

We turned and came face to face with Squadron Leader Stevenson.

"Smith attacked Sedley, sir!" said Wilson quickly. "He knocked a crate down on him. For no reason."

Stevenson looked at me, puzzled.

"I can explain, sir," I said, standing as stiffly to attention as my aching ribs would let me.

"You'll explain at a court martial, the pair of you!" snorted Stevenson. "But we'll have to save that for later. You're going to be late for the briefing." He looked down at the sprawled and groaning Sedley, then turned and glared at me and Wilson. "You two get to the Briefing Room on the double! I'll deal with Sedley."

The Big One

Wilson and I hurried to the Briefing Room. I was slowed down by the pain in my ribs, and my heavy bag, and so Wilson made it there first. By the time I walked in Wilson was with his crew, whispering to his Captain, Flying Officer Shackleton. As I came in they both shot dark looks at me, and it was obvious that Wilson had been telling Shackleton what had happened, but coloured in such a way that I was the villain of the piece.

I pushed my way through the crowd of airmen to join Bob and the rest of our crew. As I moved into a space next to Steve, the airman next to me accidentally jogged me in the ribs with his elbow, and I let out a groan. Steve turned to me, a concerned look on his face.

"What's up with you?" he asked.

Before I could reply, the briefing officer appeared from the back room and a hush fell on the crowd.

"I'll tell you later," I whispered back.

"Good afternoon, gentlemen. You may stand easy." With his pointer the briefing officer tapped a board nearby him, covered with brown cloth. "Tonight's mission," he announced.

He took the cover off the board, revealing three maps pinned to it. The first map showed the North Sea, including the British Isles, across to the Baltic and Sweden and the coast of northern Germany.

The second map showed a close-up of a section of coastline, though it wasn't one that looked familiar to me.

Red tape had been stuck across both of these maps, marking our flight plan.

The third was a detailed map of a site on the coast. To me it looked like a large camp of some sort, or an industrial complex.

I looked at Steve questioningly, and he shrugged, as puzzled as I was.

"This is part of the Baltic coast, gentlemen," announced the briefing officer. "The north coast of Germany." He tapped a spot marked on the coast with his pointer. "And this is your target for tonight. Peenemunde."

Again, the name meant nothing to me. I could tell from the blank looks on the faces surrounding me that it meant nothing to most of them, either.

The briefing officer went back to the main map and indicated the lines of red tape.

"Your flight path will take you across the North Sea, across Denmark, to a position here, 55.10 North, 07.00 East, which is where the bomber stream will be formed. You will proceed along the northern coast of Germany to the Island of Rugen, here. At this point you will turn south and head for the target."

He moved to the third map on the board – a close-up of the actual target. This map was of a peninsula with clusters of buildings in three definite sections set out along the east coast of the peninsula.

"This is Peenemunde itself, and these are your three target areas. Every one of these three targets has to be destroyed. Not just damaged, but destroyed," he repeated to emphasize the fact. "To make sure that happens, this mission is being carried out with some variations to the normal method of operation.

"First, Bomber Command is sending every plane at its disposal on this attack. That means 600 bombers. So, gentlemen, you will not be alone.

"Second, for the first time on a major raid of this sort, a Master Bomber will be employed."

At this there were some puzzled murmurs. A Master Bomber? This was a new one to us.

"I can see by your reaction that some of you are not familiar with the idea of a Master Bomber," said the briefing officer. "He will remain over the target the whole time and will direct the attack from his plane. If he should be shot down, there is a deputy Master Bomber in another plane who will take over his role. You will do as the Master Bomber says, bomb where he tells you. It is his job to make sure that the targets are obliterated. And that means accurate bombing.

"As always, squadrons of Pathfinders will be going in first to mark the targets for you, guided by the Master Bomber. They will lay down flares for you to aim at.

"In addition, you will be bombing at 6,000 feet."

This really did make us all stand up and take notice. 6,000 feet! Normally bombs were dropped from 18,000 feet. At 6,000 feet we would be flying below the level at which flak exploded.

"I know it's low," continued the briefing officer. "At 6,000 feet, you'll be able to see the colour of their eyes, and their ground defences will be able to get a closer shot at you. But that's the way it has to be, chaps. There can be no chances of messing this up tonight. The order from on high is that if we fail to destroy all three targets at Peenemunde tonight, then we have to keep going back again and again until we do. And I know you all realize this is something we can't afford. Once the Germans realize we're targeting the place, any future raids on it will fly into a brick wall of air defences that will make anything we've experienced so far look like soap bubbles.

"One other factor about tonight's raid. It's expected to be

bright moonlight, so you'll be easily spotted by the ground defences. But top brass feel that accuracy is so important that they've chosen to do it tonight because of the moonlight. You will be able to see your targets clearly. And, equally importantly, the photos that we get back from you chaps should be clear enough to show the damage done."

The more I listened, the more I realized that this was no ordinary mission. If Bomber Command were sending us out in bright moonlight, with instructions to return again and again if we failed to destroy our targets, then we were aiming at something big.

The briefing officer continued.

"To give you a hand, a diversionary raid is being flown tonight. The top brass are sending a load of Mosquitoes to attack Berlin. It's hoped that the Germans will think Berlin's your target for tonight and put their fighters there to try and defend it. It's a cover that won't last long. Once the Germans realize that Peenemunde is our real target, you can expect their fighters to come at you, and come at you hard. However, this diversion should buy you some time."

He unrolled a large sheet of paper and tacked it to the board over the map. On it was the order of flight.

"The attack will be in three waves. The first wave will consist of the Pathfinders and the Master Bomber, with a force of Stirlings, Lancasters and Halifaxes." He tapped a large area of buildings to the south of the peninsula. "They'll attack this target here at 15 minutes past midnight.

"The second wave will target these buildings here," and he tapped the middle section of buildings. "They will commence their attack at 0031. You will be in the third wave. Your target is this group of buildings here, to the north. You will begin your attack at 0042 hours. All of these bombing instructions will be given again over the target by the Master Bomber through radio contact, but with specific details taking account of the situation on the ground."

As he lowered his pointer, he said, "You don't have to be a genius to work out that by the time the third wave gets to the target, the Germans will have got wind of what's up and their fighters will be coming for you. However, we hope that their ground defences will have taken a hammering from the first two waves by the time you get over the target."

He put the cover back over the board, concealing the map and the flight order.

"That's it, chaps. Take-off commences at 2100 hours. And good luck."

Confrontation

As we left the Briefing Room, Bruce let out a laugh. "The third wave at 6,000 feet? We must be almost as mad as those Japanese kamikaze pilots."

"We'll be OK," said Bob confidently. "Like the CO said, the first two waves will have taken care of their ground defences."

"And their night fighters?" queried Steve.

Bob grinned.

"You and Bruce will take care of them, of course!" he laughed. "The Lone Cowboys of the Wild West, fastest gunslingers in the RAF!"

We were on the point of leaving the building itself, when we found our way barred by Wilson, Shackleton, and the rest of the crew of T Tommy.

"Smith," snapped Shackleton angrily, "I want a word with you."

"What's this, a lynch mob?" demanded Bob.

"I said I want a word with Smith," repeated Shackleton.

"All six of you?" queried Bob. "In that case I guess we'll all hang around to listen. Sort of evens up the score, don't you think?"

Shackleton scowled. "Your little thug here has just put my bomb aimer in the Medical Wing!" he burst out angrily.

At that all eyes turned to look at me. I even heard Bruce mutter cheerfully, "About time someone did," but Bob gestured for him to keep quiet.

"John?" asked Bob.

"I'm sorry, skipper," I admitted apologetically. "But I didn't hit Sedley. A crate fell on him."

"You knocked it on him!" burst out Wilson.

"He kicked me in the ribs, and he was about to kick me again," I countered. "I was defending myself."

Bob turned to Shackleton.

"Sounds like a fair fight to me," he shrugged. "Your man came off worse. I don't think you'd have been complaining if it had gone the other way."

"It wasn't a fair fight!" insisted Wilson. "Smith started it!"

"Two against one?" queried Steve.

"The point is I'm without a bomb aimer!" snarled Shackleton. "If I can't find one my whole crew will be grounded and off this mission tonight! One less vital bomber, thanks to your thug!"

Bob's genial good humour suddenly vanished, and his voice hardened. "Frankly, Shackleton, you've only got yourself to blame. That weasly little thug of yours has caused damage to plenty of guys on this base, and elsewhere, and you've let him get away with it. You thought it was good to have a bully like that on your crew because it frightened other people, kept your lot as top dog. Well you were wrong. Your bully met his match and came unstuck. If you miss out on tonight's mission, that's your hard luck. Just don't come running to me or anyone else on this base for sympathy."

"Hear hear, skipper!" said Steve. "It's about time someone sorted out that little worm, Sedley."

Shackleton glared at Bob, and the rest of us. "You're not going to get away with this, Smith!" he snarled at me. "I'm going to bring charges against you. Because of you we'll have one less bomber over the target tonight. That's treason. I'll have you thrown out of the service."

With that, Shackleton turned and stormed off, the rest of his crew following. Wilson was the last to go, giving me a gloating smirk just before he went.

"Thanks, skipper," I said. "I'm sorry I landed you in it, though."

"Forget it," he shrugged.

"Will he do that, though? Try and get me court-martialled?"

It was George who answered.

"I know Shackleton," he said grimly. "He'll try. Though, if you ask me, they ought to give you a medal."

I looked at George in surprise. George, one of those who

had always moaned about me being a jinx and had wanted me kicked off the crew, standing up for me like this.

"Well done, jinx," added George, and he gave me a hearty slap, which made me wince with pain.

"Sorry," said George. "I forgot about your ribs."

"Better trot along to the Medicos and get them seen to," said Bob. He looked at his watch. "Four hours to take-off. Everyone else, get ready. Remember what the briefing officer said. This is the big one."

Waiting To Go

The Medical Room was empty, all except for the MO on duty.

"Yes?" he asked.

"I think I've damaged my ribs," I said.

"How?"

I hesitated. "Someone kicked them."

"Let me guess," he said. "Would that someone be called Flight Lieutenant Sedley, by any chance?" He gestured with his thumb at the room that doubled as a small temporary ward at the back. Serious cases were sent off the base to the hospital. "I heard all about it."

"Is he badly injured?" I asked, hesitantly.

"I'm keeping him under observation," the MO told me. "Suspected concussion."

"Will he be able to fly tonight?"

"Is he one of your crew?" demanded the MO.

"No," I replied.

"Then I'll leave my answer to his Captain," he said tersely. "Now, either you're here to discuss other people's symptoms, or for me to look at your ribs. Which is it?"

"My ribs," I replied.

"Right," he said crisply. "Get your clothes off and let's have a look at them."

It hurt as I took off my tunic and peeled off my shirt and vest. The whole of my side was discoloured with a large multicoloured bruise, mainly purple, but with hints of yellow, green, blue, red, and even black.

"Hmmm," murmured the MO. "Now that is some kick. And Sedley did this?"

I nodded, then gave a yelp as he prodded the bruise.

"You've got two cracked ribs," he said. "You're off duty."

It was strange. I had come back to the base determined to tell Bob Campbell that I was quitting his crew. Now my damaged ribs gave me the perfect opportunity for not flying tonight. But instead of feeling relieved, I felt cheated. If I didn't fly tonight, then neither would the rest of S Sarah. And from what the briefing officer had told us, this would be the most important mission we'd ever flown. If I used my ribs as an excuse, I would feel like a coward ducking out. I didn't know what made this mission so important, but it was. And S Sarah had to be on it.

I shook my head.

"I'm sorry," I said. "That's not possible. I've got to fly tonight!"

"With two cracked ribs?" he queried.

"Other chaps have flown with a lot worse than this. Can't you just strap them up?"

The MO hesitated, then nodded.

"All right," he said. "And I'll give you some painkillers."

"Not too strong," I said. "I'm going to need a clear head tonight."

I sat in the chair as the MO put some ointment on the bruise, and then proceeded to wrap bandages round and round my chest. I began to feel like one of those Egyptian mummies.

When he was finished he gave me two tablets.

"Here," he said. "Take one now, take the other if the pain gets bad later on."

I swallowed the tablet and put the other away for later. Although I had no intention of taking it. I had to be fully alert tonight, even if it did mean being in pain.

As I left, the MO said quietly: "Good luck tonight."

I found most of the rest of my crew in the mess hall. George and Andrew had taken over a ping-pong table and were playing a very serious game of table tennis.

Steve and Bruce were playing a game of darts against a pair of gunners from another crew, with many jokes being made about accuracy. Wally was reading a book.

"Where's Bob?" I asked him.

"He went off," said Wally. "Said he's got some business to attend to."

With that Wally returned to his reading.

I hesitated, and then, before I could stop myself, I blurted out, "Do you really think I'm a jinx, Wally?"

Wally put down his book and looked at me.

"Yes," he said. "I do. I think you're unlucky."

"Then maybe I should quit being part of an air crew," I said.

"Maybe you should," said Wally. "But not tonight."

I looked at him, intrigued. There was something in his tone that told me Wally knew more about this raid than he was letting on.

"Why?" I asked. "If I'm a jinx, then maybe it's safer for everyone else on our crew if I stand down now. Before S Sarah goes up tonight."

Wally looked around to make sure that no one else was listening to our conversation, then he motioned me to sit down next to him.

"I don't care if you're the worst luck that's ever been, and on the way back we all get shot down," he said quietly. "Peenemunde has got to be put out of action."

"How come you know so much about it?" I asked. "Most of the rest of us have never even heard of the place."

Wally hesitated again, then he said: "Because I've got a cousin in a Reconnaissance Unit. He told me about this Peenemunde place. Intelligence was received that they were developing rocket bombs there which could be fired from Germany and hit London, Birmingham Glasgow. All Britain's major cities.

"Can you imagine the terrible effect they would have if they got into production?" continued Wally. "The Germans would be able to blitz Britain with ease and we'd have no defence against them. The War would be over in months. Maybe weeks."

"Are you sure these things actually exist?" I asked, shocked. Wally nodded.

"Ronnie flew a mission flying over this Peenemunde place, taking photos. The intelligence reports turned out to be true. The rockets are there all right. Ever since he told me about them, I've been wondering how our side would deal with them. Well, now we know. It's up to us to destroy them. And the factory that's making them."

I sat there, stunned at the power of these unmanned long-range rocket bombs.

"Normally I wouldn't have said anything," added Wally. "You know the rules."

I nodded. The reason none of us were ever told the reason behind a mission was because, if we were shot down and captured by the Germans, we couldn't tell them anything and their intelligence services wouldn't know what our intelligence knew.

"But I'm telling you because I don't want you quitting now and leaving us high and dry," said Wally. "You may be a jinx, but tonight we need every plane we've got over Peenemunde. Tonight is the night that this war is won or lost."

Peenemunde

Night fell as we left England. We flew over the North Sea towards Denmark, heading for our assembly point, 300 miles from the coast of England and sixty miles from Denmark. The moon came out and shone brightly, almost as clear as day. Just as Bomber Command had predicted, there was no cloud at all to give us cover. Although it made flying easier, I felt terribly exposed.

During this first part of the journey, which took an hour and a half, we met no German fighters. My thoughts turned to the pilots flying the decoy Mosquito raid on Berlin. They were acting as sitting ducks to pull the German fighters away from us.

We crossed Denmark at 18,000 feet, the drone of our four engines filling the interior of the plane. As we left the Danish coast Andrew and the other bomb aimers dropped their Window to confuse the German radar.

My headphones crackled, and then I heard the voice of the Master Bomber giving instructions for us to form the bomber stream. Bob put our Lancaster into a circle, along with other Lancs, and one by one we joined a queue of flying bombers. Above us, below us, and on either side of us were more planes. It was like a huge flying traffic jam in the sky, three or four planes deep.

Then we were off, heading along the northern coast of Germany in long lines. Bright moonlight made it easy to see and identify the areas below us. I bet that Wally had never had such an easy job navigating; all his identifying points were as clear as day below us: islands, rivers, even the lights of Arkona, the town which was at the northern point of the island of Rugen.

"Third wave, turn and head for the target!" came our instructions.

"Roger!" responded Bob. Then, to us, he added: "Here we go, chaps!"

As we flew in, we could see Peenemunde from far away. The ground was burning for miles in different directions following the attacks by the first two waves. It was so bright I could even make out buildings, wire fences, and where the camp became forest. However, visibility was starting to become a problem because of the smoke pouring up from the ground.

As we came in, the second wave of bombers was just leaving the target area. The Luftwaffe fighters had also just arrived, brought in by reports of the attack.

A German fighter was attacking a Halifax from the second wave as we arrived. More air battles were going on all around us.

The whole of the night sky above Peenemunde was like a mad fairground: the huge bombers circling and diving, each one being chased by the smaller fighter planes, the sky lit up with bright moonlight, searchlights from the ground, the multi colours of the flashes and flares from the Pathfinders, streams of tracer as gunners from both sides poured bullets at their enemies. The sound of gunfire, explosions, the noise of hundreds of engines was deafening.

As Bob turned our plane to bring it down towards the target, I saw one of the Lancasters near us suddenly turn into a ball of flame as two German fighters hit it from close range.

I watched as the plane fell out of the sky towards the ground, burning fiercely all the while, and again the thought hit me: "That could have been us."

Over the R/T we heard the Master Bomber's voice, cool and calm as he gave us our instructions. I was filled with admiration for this man, talking so calmly and confidently. We'd only just arrived. He had been circling the target below us for at least the last half an hour, under attack the whole time, yet from the tone of his voice he might have been reading the weather report.

I heard Wally's voice loud and clear, bringing us down towards the target: "12,000 feet ... 10,000 ... 8,000 ..."

It was nerve-wracking coming down to this height. Flak

from the anti-aircraft guns usually exploded beneath us. Now it was exploding above and all around us. "6,000 feet."

Andrew took over, checking the target through his bomb aimer's sights.

"Left ... left ... steady ... right..."

With so many bombers around us, also dropping their lethal cargoes, it struck me there was the danger of our being bombed by one of our own planes flying above us.

"Identify your marker!" came the Master Bomber's voice over the R/T. "Wave three, blue flares!"

Down below, through the smoke, the different coloured flares could be seen against the background of the burning buildings.

At this low height I could even see the runway of the airfield next to the area.

"Fighter coming in!" reported Bruce.

There was the chatter chatter chatter of his guns as he fired at the German. Suddenly our plane gave a lurch.

"What's happened?" called Bob, now struggling with the controls.

"He hit us!" came Bruce's voice. "Sparks coming from the port engine! I think we're on fire!"

Not again! I groaned inwardly, and shuddered at the thought that my bad luck had ruined this mission for us before we reached our target.

I checked the control panel. The instruments showed a loss of power on the outward port engine. The temperature of the coolant was rising. We were in trouble.

Bob was obviously now having difficulty holding the Lancaster. I could feel the vibration as he fought to keep it on a level course.

"John…!" commanded Bob.

"Got it, skipper," I said.

I switched off the burning engine's master fuel cock, turned on the engine's fire-extinguisher to put out the flames, then switched off.

Bob now re-trimmed the aircraft to take account of the fact that we were only flying on three engines.

By now the remaining ground defences around our target had really opened up, hurling everything they had at us. Flak was exploding all around us.

"Bomb doors open!"

The plane shuddered and its nose pushed up as the bomb doors in our belly opened. The shell bursts around us were rocking us from side to side.

"Steady…!" came Andrew's voice, now tense as he prepared to let them go.

Then the Lancaster seemed to lift up into the sky.

"Bombs gone!" came Andrew's voice. "Hold steady for the camera!"

Bob struggled to hold the plane steady until we were sure the camera had recorded where our bombs had landed.

"OK, boys, that's it!" came Bob's voice. "We're heading for home!"

As Bob turned the Lanc to head north, there was a sudden explosion from our starboard and bursts of tracer tore through our fuselage.

The next second we were dropping out of the sky.

On Fire Again!

I turned and looked at Bob, and saw him slumped in his seat, the dark liquid of blood seeping through his flying jacket.

"I'm hit!" he gasped.

Before I could even move, Bob had managed to struggle painfully up and grab the controls with one gloved hand. His other arm hung down uselessly. Somehow he managed to pull up the Lanc and stop us going into a spin and spiralling into the ground.

"Shove over, skip!" I said. "I'll take over."

"I can't shove anywhere, John." Bob forced the words out through gritted teeth.

I tore off my straps and then set to work on his. As gently as I could I eased him from his seat and lay him on the floor. Then I slid into his seat and gripped the controls. Jinx or not, I was going to do my utmost to get this plane and my crewmates back. Alive.

"What's happening up front?" came Steve's voice through my headphones. "This thing's going all over the place."

"Skipper's been hit," I replied.

"Hit?!" echoed Steve. "So who's flying this thing?"

"I am," I said.

"Have you ever flown a Lancaster before, John?" came George's worried voice.

"Of course," I said confidently.

But only in training, I almost added. Perhaps this wasn't a good time to be honest with them. Not with just three engines out of four working, and under attack from German fighters.

"Is Bob alive?" asked Wally.

I looked down at Bob lying on the floor of the plane, his eyes closed, but breathing.

"So far," I said.

"Look out, Bruce!" came Steve's sudden shout. "Bandits coming from starboard…!"

I heard the rat tat tat tat tat chatter chatter chatter from both their guns. Then a shudder from the plane as I felt the tail take a burst of tracer.

"We're hit!" Bruce shouted.

"Position?" I asked.

"The hydraulic lines have been shot! Oil's coming out…"

"Get out of the turret, Bruce!" I shouted urgently. "Someone get down there with a fire extinguisher!"

"It's OK—" began Bruce, then he suddenly gave a yell of alarm. "We're on fire!"

"Get out of that turret!" I shouted again.

I could feel the big plane pulling, wanting to go into a spin and dive down, but I fought it, kicked it all the way to hold it level.

Memories of the fire on the earlier Lanc came flooding back to me. I thought of Danny at the controls as we came in from the North Sea on fire. Had it been like this for him? Struggling with the plane all the way while the rear turret burned?

"The fire's getting bigger!" yelled Bruce.

"On my way!" shouted George. "Extinguisher coming!"

"Nearing the coast," came Wally's voice. "Sea ahead. If we're going to bale out it'd be better to do it over the land. Dropping into the sea at night like this, especially one as cold as the Baltic, we'll be drowned for sure."

"You bale out," I said. "I'm staying. Bob can't jump and I'm going to get him home."

There was a brief pause, then Andrew said: "Forget any thought of baling out. I'm with you, John."

"Can we have some more help here with this fire?!" shouted George. "We need another extinguisher!"

"I'm on my way!" said Andrew.

We flew out over the German coast and over the sea. Then I banked to port and set course towards Denmark.

Luckily for us the German fighters had pulled back to stay and attack the bombers that were left over Peenemunde.

"How's that fire?!" I shouted desperately.

"Fire in the rear turret's out!" called Bruce.

Thank heavens for that! I thought as a feeling of relief flooded over me. Now all I have to do is get this crippled machine back three hundred miles on just three engines.

"Well done, fellas," I said. "The worst is over."

And then one of the three remaining engines shut down.

No Engines!

"I think I'd better let you chaps know," I announced, doing my best to appear calm and in control, "that we've just lost another engine."

Silence. No one spoke, and I realized they must have all been thinking the worst. They were flying with a man who was cursed, and were all going to die.

"It's the inner starboard engine," I added, "so we still have a chance."

If it had been the remaining engine on the port side I would have been in really serious trouble, trying to hold the plane level and straight with two engines dead on the same wing.

"Can you fix it?" came George's voice.

"Not while flying it at the same time," I said. "With a bit of luck I should be able to get us home, but if we lose another engine we might have to ditch. So make sure you've got everything ready."

"What about Bob?" asked Steve.

"Don't worry," I said determinedly. "I'll look after Bob. Just keep a watch out for German fighters. It's going to be difficult doing any evasive flying from now on."

And so I flew the Lancaster on across the landmass of Denmark, across the North Sea, and that wonderful machine stayed in the air, despite having two engines gone, holes throughout its body, and the rear turret hanging off.

Luckily we had no further sightings of German fighters for the rest of the trip. Bruce came up to the front and made Bob as comfortable as he could, stripping his shirt and jacket off him and doing his best to stop the bleeding, but Bob was obviously in a bad way.

As we neared the coast of Lincolnshire, George managed to raise Wickenby on the radio. He told them of our situation and told them that we needed an ambulance standing by for Bob.

I kept my attention firmly fixed on the control panel, gauging how much fuel we had left. We'd lost some from one of the tanks during the attack, and I felt a sick feeling in my stomach as I realized that we might not have enough fuel to make it back.

I glanced quickly down at Bob, lying on the floor just behind me. Bruce was sitting beside the skipper and gave me a tentative thumbs up. So far, Bob was still alive.

"English coast approaching!" announced Wally.

It was at that moment that the outward starboard engine cut out.

The plane gave a lurch to port, dragged by the force of

the one remaining engine on the port wing, and I fought the controls to bring it back to starboard, and then level again.

"One engine left, chaps!" I announced. "Course for base, Wally?"

Wally gave me the course setting and I adjusted our direction accordingly. We were still three miles from the base when the final engine coughed, and then stopped.

"That's it!" I said. "From now on we're in a glider! Find something to brace yourselves against!"

A glider is a special sort of plane. Light. Wide-winged. Made to fly on thermals, uplifting currents of air. A 25-ton Lancaster is not a glider, but I somehow made S Sarah glide. Banking and turning into currents of air where I could, easing her to port and starboard to catch up-currents as we came down down down.

"Wickenby dead ahead, John!" called Wally. "Dead ahead!"

"Hold firm! I'm putting her down. It's going to be a bumpy landing!"

Lower we came, lower and lower, my eyes glued to the lights of Wickenby ahead. With no engines to act as air brakes, it was all down to the flaps.

Suddenly the lights that marked either side of the runway were racing up towards me.

"Here we go!" I shouted.

I put the flaps down to reduce our speed, and then there was a thud as our wheels hit the tarmac. A slight bounce, and then we were down. I eased on the brakes, hoping that the bullets that had damaged our fuel lines and the rear turret hydraulic system hadn't also cut our braking system. But the brakes bit, and held. I released them momentarily to avoid skidding the Lanc on the runway, then put them on firmly again, and we rolled to a stop.

"Yes!!" came Steve's joyous shout through my headphones. "The boy wonder's done it! We're home!"

Before we opened the door, an ambulance was already speeding towards us, its emergency lights flashing.

"Well done, John," whispered a voice.

It was Bob. His eyes were open, and although his voice was weak he managed to force a smile.

I knelt down beside him.

"Thanks, skipper," I said. "You'd have landed us better, though."

"I doubt it," he said.

Just then the Medical Orderlies appeared in the plane.

"Stand aside," ordered one briskly. "We'll take care of him!"

I moved aside so they could get Bob out and on to a stretcher.

As we walked across the tarmac towards the main buildings, the rest of the crew were in jubilant mood.

"We did it!" crowed Bruce. "We've just taken part in the most important and dangerous mission I've ever been involved in, and we made it home on a plane with no engines. And we've all come home alive!"

"Thanks to John!" beamed George.

With that he slapped me heartily on the back. It was only then, as a sudden pain kicked in as he thumped me, that I remembered my two cracked ribs. But all at once, in the light of what we'd just been through, a couple of cracked ribs seemed pretty unimportant. We were home, and safe!

"Still think John's a jinx, Wally?" demanded Andrew.

I turned and looked at Wally, curious as to what his answer would be. Wally looked at me, then grinned and shook his head.

"Not after what he did," he said. Then he added: "Maybe there are really no such things as jinxes. I guess we're all lucky or unlucky at different times. Lucky for us, today was one of John's lucky days."

And Wally stuck out his hand towards me.

"I'm sorry if I ever called you a jinx," he said. "Mates?"

"Never anything but mates, Wally," I smiled as I shook his hand firmly.

Jinx No More

Next morning some of the delight of the night before had faded. Yes, I'd brought us back home, but there was still the problem about Sedley looming over my head. Pilot Officer Shackleton wouldn't have been pleased to have missed out on the Peenemunde raid. I was sure he would have been already carrying out his threat to have me court-martialled. If that happened I'd be thrown out of the service. It felt especially bitter to me, just when the doubters like Wally had finally accepted me as a vital member of the crew.

I was moping around feeling miserable for myself, when Steve called at my quarters and let me know that Bob Campbell was on the road to recovery.

"He's sitting up in bed and complaining that he needs to get out and back in a plane," said Steve. "The docs have told him he'll just have to shut up and stay there until they give him the all-clear. But you know what Bob's like."

I did, and I chuckled at the thought of Bob in hospital, bandaged and stitched up, and making life miserable for the orderlies as he insisted he was fighting fit.

"Is he receiving visitors?" I asked. "If so I'll pop in and see him."

"He is, and the one visitor he wants to see is you," said Steve. "So I'd get over there before the medics decide to order a complete rest for him."

For a man who'd been shot, Bob looked surprisingly well when I went to see him. He was pale, and hooked up to tubes, but his old character was well in evidence.

"So you turned our Lanc into a glider," he grinned when he saw me. "That'll take a bit of living down from the other pilots!"

"They're just jealous," I grinned back. "How are you, skipper?"

"For a man with lots of holes in him, not bad at all," said Bob. "Actually, John, I asked Steve to send you over for two reasons. The first is so I can thank you. You saved my life. All our lives."

"You would have done the same," I said.

"Maybe," said Bob. "The other reason is Sedley."

"Oh," I said, and I felt my face fall. "Is there going to be a court martial?"

Bob shook his head.

"No," he said. "That's what I wanted to let you know."

I was stunned.

"But Flying Officer Shackleton…" I began.

"Flying Officer Shackleton is a sensible man when you put things to him," said Bob. "Before we set out for Peenemunde last night I had a word with both the Station Commander, and with Shackleton. Shackleton finally admitted that Sedley is a bad lot. The Station Commander's always suspected it, but hasn't had any proof, until now. So, Sedley's going to be kicked out. And you're in the clear."

I felt a big grin spread all over my face.

"Careful," warned Bob. "If you're suddenly going to start slapping me on the back, remember, I'm an invalid whose still got bits of metal in him."

"Thanks, skipper!" I said, grateful and relieved.

"Now you've said your thanks you can leave and let the patient get some rest," said a voice.

I turned and saw that a doctor had come in.

"I'm just going," I said.

"This is John Smith," introduced Bob.

"Ah yes," said the doctor. "The young hero. The man who brought in a plane without engines. The whole station's talking about you. Well done, young man, but now, as I say, my patient does need his rest."

I gave Bob a wave, and then left.

As I walked away from the hospital wing, I felt as if I was walking on air. Not only was I no longer threatened with a court martial, I was also no longer John Smith, the jinx. I was now John Smith, the man who'd brought his mates back.

PEENEMUNDE AND AFTER

On the night of 17th August 1943 a decoy raid was launched on Berlin to draw the German night fighters away from the Baltic coast, and the real target for that night's bombing mission, the Nazis' Secret Weapons Research Establishment at Peenemunde on the Baltic coast. False information had already been leaked by the British about the raid on Berlin.

Three waves of bombers, 596 in all, were sent to attack Peenemunde. They included a Master Bomber and a wave of Pathfinders, whose job was to set down markers on the target.

During the raid on Peenemunde, nearly 2,000 tons of bombs landed around the three main targets: the assembly works, the drawing offices, and the administration block. 735 people at the factory were killed, including many key scientists.

Of the 596 bombers which took part in the mission, 40 were shot down and 32 badly damaged, most of them in the third wave.

According to Goebbels' diary, the raid caused drastic delays in the flying bomb programme: "The

English raids have thrown our preparations back 4 to 7, or even 8 weeks, so that we can't possibly count on reprisals before the end of January." In fact, the flying bomb programme developing and using the V-2 rockets was delayed by over four months, the first rockets not being used until September 1944.

The V rockets were devastatingly effective missiles. The earlier V-1, also known as the flying bomb or doodlebug, was powered by jet motor and carried a 1-ton warhead. It was launched from a fixed ramp. The V-1s were first launched against Britain from June 1944. During 1944-1945 about 9,000 V-1 rockets were fired on southern England. Of these, about 4,500 were destroyed by anti-aircraft fire or by the RAF's fastest fighters.

The V-2 was a much more dangerous weapon. Once it was launched it could not be easily stopped. The V-2 was a liquid-fuelled rocket capable of supersonic speeds, and able to travel greater distances. There was no effective air defence against the V-2.

THE SIGNIFICANCE OF PEENEMUNDE

The destruction of the factory at Peenemunde delayed the launching of the V-2 rockets long enough for the Allies to inflict serious defeats on the German war effort, so that by the time they came into use late in 1944 they were mainly a "last-gasp" form of counter-attack by the Germans, rather than part of a major invasion offensive.

If the V-2 had come into operation in 1943 the civilian casualties in Britain would have been far far heavier than they actually were and the war could well have been lost.

The deaths of many of the key scientists during the raid on Peenemunde, and especially that of Dr Thiel, the propulsion specialist, halted the development of many new weapons which would have been vital to the German war effort, including the *Wasserfall* anti-aircraft rocket and the A-9 two stage rocket, which was intended to reach any part of Britain as far away as Glasgow.

THE PEENEMUNDE RAID – THE STATISTICS

a) Tonnage of bombs dropped during the raid:

1,528 tons of high explosives

267 tons of incendiaries

b) RAF casualties:

During this raid the RAF lost 290 air crew, 288 from Bomber Command and 2 from Fighter Command.

Bomber Crew Casualties 1939–1945

Those who volunteered for Bomber Command knew that their chances of surviving the war were very slim.

A tour of duty consisted of 30 missions. Many aircrew flew two or three tours of duty.

In any 2-year cycle of service, out of every 100 airmen who flew with Bomber Command, the following statistics show what happened to them, and their chances of survival:

Killed in operation	51
Killed in crashes in Britain	9
Seriously injured in crashes	3
Prisoners of war	12
Shot down and evaded capture	1
Survived unharmed	24

In other words, the airmen who flew with Bomber Command had only a 24% chance of surviving physically unscathed, and there was a 60% chance of them being killed.

Bomber Command Air Crew Killed 1939–1945

Royal Air Force	38,462
Royal Canadian Air Force	9,919
Royal Australian Air Force	4,050
Royal New Zealand Air Force	1,679
Polish Air Force	929
Other	500
Total:	55,539

BOMBER COMMAND – BOMBERS OF THE RAF

AVRO LANCASTER MARK I

Type: 7-seat heavy night bomber

Power: 4 x 1640 hp (1,223 kW) Rolls Royce Merlin XX, 22 or 24 12-cylinder V engines

Performance: Max speed: 287 mph (462 km/h)

                Initial climb rate: 250 ft (76 m) per minute

                Service ceiling: 19,00 0ft (5,790 m)

Range (with a 12,000 lb bomb load): 1,730 miles (2,784 km)

Weight: Empty: 37,000 lb (16,783 kg)

          Maximum take-off: 65,000 lb (29,484 kg)

Dimensions: Wingspan: 102 ft (31.09 m)

                Length: 69 ft 6 in (21.18 m)

                Height: 20 ft 6 in (6.25 m)

Armaments: 2 x 0.303 trainable machine guns in the nose turret

2 x 0.303 trainable machine guns in the dorsal turret

4 x 0.303 trainable machine guns in the tail turret

Provision for 1 x 0.303 trainable machine guns in the ventral turret

Internal bomb load of 18,000 lb (8,165 kg)

The Avro Lancaster was the most successful heavy night bomber used by the RAF in World War II. It was a development of the Avro Manchester medium bomber, which had not been a success because of problems with its Vulture engines. The revised engine power of 4 x Rolls-Royce Merlin Vee engines were a major factor in giving the Lancaster its celebrated stature. The Lancaster first flew in January 1941 and entered service at the start of 1942. Few changes other than minor engine and equipment details were made to the original design for the different Marks. In all, 7,378 Lancasters were produced.

AVRO LANCASTER MARK VI

Type: 5-seat special mission bomber

Power: 4 x 1,640 hp (1,223 kW) Rolls Royce Merlin 85/87 12-cylinder V engines

Performance: Max speed: 345 mph (555 km/h)

             Initial climb rate: 250 ft (76 m) per minute

             Service ceiling: 21,418 ft (6,500 m)

Range (with a 22,000 lb bomb load): 1,550 miles (2,494 km)

Weight: Empty: 35,475 lb (16,083 kg)

           Maximum take-off: 72,000 lb (32,695 kg)

Dimensions: Wingspan: 102 ft (31.09 m)

             Length: 69 ft 6 in (21.18 m)

             Height: 20 ft 6 in (6.25 m)

Armaments: 4 x 0.303 trainable machine guns in the tail turret

Nine Avro Lancaster Mark VI were created to carry out electronic counter-measures for the Pathfinder Force. They were converted from Mark I and Mark III Lancasters by re-engining them with two super-charged Merlin 85.87 in circular cowling. With 4-bladed propellers and all armaments except the tail guns removed, the Mark VI had superb performance. The Mk VI also had an improved version of the H2S bombing radar, which was protected by a central fairing. Aircraft operating as Pathfinders had their fins painted with high-visibility stripes so that they could be easily identified by other Lancasters.

VICKERS WELLINGTON B. MARKS I TO X

Type: 6-seat medium bomber
Power: 2 x 1675 hp (1249 kW) Bristol Hercules XI or XVI 14Her-cylinder 2-row radial engines
Performance: Max speed: 255 mph (410 km/h)
                     Initial climb rate: 15,000 ft (4,750 m) in 27 minutes 42 seconds
                     Service ceiling: 22,000 ft (6,705 m)
Range (with a 1,500 lb bomb load): 1,885 miles (3,033.5 km)
Weight: Empty: 22,474 lb (10,194 kg)
          Maximum take-off: 36,500 lb (16,556 kg)
Dimensions: Wingspan: 86 ft 2 in (26.26 m)
                     Length: 64 ft 7 in (19.68 m)
                     Height: 17 ft 5 in (5.31 m)
Armaments: 2 x 0.303 trainable forward-firing machine guns in the nose turret
2 x 0.303 trainable rearward-firing machine guns in the tail turret
1 x 0.303 trainable lateral-firing machine gun in each beam position
Internal bomb load of 4,500 lb (2,041 kg)

The Wellington entered service in 1938, and was one of the RAF's most important planes at the start of World War II. It was Britain's most important bomber until the four-engined heavies came into operation in 1942. 11,461 Wellingtons were produced between 1938 and 1945.

HANDLEY PAGE HALIFAX

Type: 7-seat heavy bomber

Power: 4 x 1615 hp (1204 kW) Bristol Hercules VI or XVI 14Her-cylinder 2-row radial engines

Performance: Max speed: 282 mph (454 km/h)

                Initial climb rate: 20,000 ft (6,095 m) in 37 minutes 30 seconds

                Service ceiling: 24,000 ft (7,315 m)

Range (with a 7,000 lb bomb load): 1,985 miles (3,194 km)

Weight: Empty: 42,500 lb (19,278 kg)

                Maximum take-off: 65,000 lb (29,484 kg)

Dimensions: Wingspan: 98 ft 8 in (30.07 m)

(in some later models: 103 ft 8 in (31.59 km)

        Length: 71 ft 4 in (21.74 m)

        Height: 20 ft 1 in (6.12 m)

Armaments: 1 x 0.303 trainable forward-firing machine gun in the nose turret

4 x 0.303 trainable machine guns in the dorsal turret

2 x 0.303 trainable machine guns in the tail turret

Internal bomb load of 14,500 lb (6,577 kg)

The Halifax was the RAF's main heavy bomber after the Lancaster. As with the Lancasters, Halifaxes were also used as Pathfinders. The first prototype Halifaxes flew in 1938, entering service in 1940. Because of the superiority of the Lancaster as a heavy bomber, many of the early Halifaxes were converted for other uses, such as electronic counter-measures to upset the German radar systems, and also for glider-towing, and as troop transports.

SHORT STIRLING MARKS I TO V

Type: 7/8-seat heavy bomber

Power: 4 x 1650 hp (1230 kW) Bristol Hercules XVI 14Her-cylinder 2-row radial engines

Performance: Max speed: 270 mph (434 km/h)
                Initial climb rate: 800 ft (244 m) per minute
                Service ceiling: 17,000 ft (5,180 m)

Range (with a 3,500 lb bomb load): 2,010 miles (3,235 km)

Weight: Empty: 46,900 lb (21,274 kg)
         Maximum take-off: 70,000 lb (31,752 kg)

Dimensions: Wingspan: 99 ft 1 in (30.20 m)
                Length: 87 ft 3 in (26.59 m)
                Height: 22 ft 9 in (6.93 m)

Armaments: 2 x 0.303 trainable forward-firing machine gun in the nose turret

2 x 0.303 trainable machine guns in the dorsal turret

4 x 0.303 trainable rearward-firing machine guns in the tail turret
Internal bomb load of 14,000 lb (6,350 kg)

The Stirling was the first 4-engined bomber to enter service with RAF's Bomber
Command during World War II, in August 1940. It was also the first 4-engined
bomber to be designed as such, because both the Lancaster and the Halifax were
developments of earlier 2-engined designs. Production of various types resulted
in 2,374 Stirlings being produced, 579 of which were for paratroop and glider-
towing aircraft without nose and dorsal turrets.

ARMSTRONG WHITWORTH WHITLEY
Type: 5-seat long-range night bomber
Power: 2 x 1145 hp (854 kW) Rolls Royce Merlin X 12-cylinder V engines
Performance: Max speed: 230 mph (370 km/h)
                 Initial climb rate: 15,000 ft (4,570 m) in 16 minutes
                 Service ceiling: 26,000 ft (7,925 m)
Range (with a 3,000 lb bomb load): 1650 miles (2,655 km)
Weight: Empty: 19,350 lb (8,777 kg)
         Maximum take-off: 33,500 lb (15,195 kg)
Dimensions: Wingspan: 84 ft (25.6 m)
                Length: 70 ft 6 in (21.49 m)
                Height: 1 5ft (4.57 m)
Armaments: 1 x 0.303 trainable forward-firing machine gun in the nose turret

4 x 0.303 trainable rearward-firing machine guns in the tail turret
Internal bomb load of 7,000 lb (3175 kg)

Although it was considered to be obsolescent at the start of World War II, the Whitley was one of Bomber Command's key planes in the early days of the war in 1939. It entered service in 1937. Its primary role was as a night bomber. Later during the war, as the Lancaster and the Halifaxes superseded it, the Whitleys continued service under Coastal Command in the role of patrol and anti-submarine planes. By the end of the war they were mainly used for glider-towing and for paratroop training.

AVRO MANCHESTER

Type: 7-seat medium bomber
Power: 2 x 1760 hp (1312 kW) Rolls Royce Vulture 24 -cylinder X-type engines
Performance: Max speed: 265 mph (426 km/h)
                Service ceiling: 19,200 ft (5,850 m)
Range (with a 8,100 lb bomb load): 1,630 miles (2,623 km)
Weight: Empty: 29,432 lb (13,350 kg)
          Maximum take-off: 56,000 lb (25,402 kg)
Dimensions: Wingspan: 90 ft 1 in (27.46 m)
                Length: 69 ft 4.25 in (21.14 m)
                Height: 19 ft 6 in (5.94 m)
Armaments: 2 x 0.303 trainable machine guns in the nose turret

2 x 0.303 trainable machine guns in a ventral turret (later replaced by a dorsal turret)
4 x 0.303 trainable rearward-firing machine guns in the tail turret
Internal bomb load of 10,350 lb (4,695 kg)

The Manchester, produced by the Avro Company, was built to specifications asked for by the Air Ministry in 1936. It first flew in July 1939 and 200 were initially built. However, although the Manchester had an ideal airframe, major problems with its unreliable Vulture engines led to it being phased out and retired from active service in June 1942. The Manchester is important, however, because the company added 4 Merlin engines to the Manchester's basic design to develop the legendary Lancaster.

BRISTOL BLENHEIM Mk IV

Type: 3-seat light bomber
Power: 2 x 9955 hp (742 kW) Bristol Mercury 9Her-cylinder single-row radial engines
Performance: Max speed: 2,566 mph (428 km/h)
                 Initial climb rate: 15,000 ft (457 m) per minute
                 Service ceiling: 22,000 ft (6,705 m)
Range (with a 1,000 lb bomb load): 1,460 miles (2,350 km)
Weight: Empty: 9,823 lb (44,456 kg)
         Maximum take-off: 15,000 lb (6,840 kg)

Dimensions: Wingspan: 56 ft 4 in (17.17 m)
                 Length: 42 ft 7 in (12.98 m)
                 Height: 12 ft 9.5 in (3.90 m)

Armaments: 1 x 0.303 fixed forward-firing machine guns in the leading edge of the port wing

2 x 0.303 trainable machine guns in the dorsal turret

2 x 0.303 trainable rearward-firing machine gun in undernose blister positions

Internal bomb load of 1,000 lb (454 kg)

The Blenheim Mark IV was a development on from the earlier Mark I. The Mark IV improved on the Mark I by having engines with more power, and also greater fuel capacity, thus increasing its range. Additionally the forward fuselage was lengthened by some 3 feet (0.91 m) to include a navigator's station under a glazed surface. The Blenheim Mark IV entered production in 1939 and by the outbreak of war the RAF had 13 squadrons of these light bombers.

DEPTH CHARGE DANGER

THE BATTLE IN THE NORTH SEA

At the start of the Second World War, Britain had a ten-to-one warship superiority over Germany. But this advantage was misleading: many of Britain's ships were old and coming to the end of their serviceable lives. Most of Germany's vessels were of modern design and construction. The prize possessions of the German Navy were the *Bismarck* and the *Tirpitz*. These sister battleships, with their specially strengthened hull armour, were the mightiest warships afloat at the time. The British warships, with their thinner hulls, would have been at a disadvantage in any major sea battle with these two giants.

The *Bismarck* was sunk by the British Navy in May 1941 after a long battle on the open seas against a superior number of British ships. The Germans learnt a valuable lesson from that defeat and, as a result, they moored the *Tirpitz* in the safety of the Norwegian fjords, ready to attack Allied Arctic Convoys.

These Arctic Convoys sailed across the perilous frozen North Sea from Great Britain to the USSR, the

Union of Soviet Socialist Republics (Russia). Russia was fighting the Germans on the Eastern Front, and was in need of the vital supplies brought by these convoys.

As well as the *Tirpitz*, two other heavy battleships, *Scharnhorst* and *Lutzow*, were part of the German North Sea fleet, along with U-boat wolf packs.

The RAF launched a number of air attacks on the *Tirpitz*, but she was protected by the high sides and narrow approaches to the fjords, and by strong anti-aircraft defences. All these attacks failed.

Surface assaults from the sea were out of the question because of the superior power of the *Tirpitz*'s armaments and its natural protection from the fjords. An attack by conventional submarines was also impossible because the entrances to the fjords that housed the *Tirpitz* were protected by two layers of heavy metal netting suspended in the water – one anti-submarine, the other anti-torpedo.

In October 1942 the Royal Navy sent out a small fleet of "Chariots" (unarmed torpedoes that could carry two divers). The plan was to attach limpet mines to the *Tirpitz*'s hull. This attack also failed.

The *Tirpitz* seemed to be invincible.

Meanwhile, the battle in the North Sea raged:

Allied shipping losses mounted as a result of German U-boat attacks. British submarines sent to protect the convoys were themselves hunted by the German warships and U-boats.

By Spring 1943 the Allies appeared to be losing the war of the North Sea. May of that year was to be the turning point.

Under Attack

KERRBOOOOOOSHHHHH!

The force of the exploding depth charge hurled our submarine violently sideways. I grabbed frantically on to the periscope housing to stop myself being thrown against the metal walls.

Commander Walters gestured for everyone to stay silent. We knew that the two German ships above would be listening out for us with their hydrophones. No one dared to move in case they made a noise.

Kerboooooooooooshhhhhhhh!

Another explosion, but further away this time. The submarine rocked as the force of the blast pushed us backwards through the water. Chief Stannard, our petty officer, winked at me confidently. I didn't feel so optimistic. Here I was, Lieutenant John Smith, twenty years old, on my third voyage in the submarine *Sandtail*, trapped between the Germans sixty feet above and the icy depths below. My first two voyages had been without major incident. We'd gone home empty-handed after the first, and had sunk two tankers on the second. This third trip we had ventured almost up to the Norwegian coast, where we'd had major successes, sinking four supply ships.

In retaliation the Germans had sent out spotter planes and anti-submarine craft to look for us. Two hours earlier a Dornier bomber had spotted us cruising just below the surface of the water and had dropped depth charges. The charges had been set too deep. In one way this was fortunate because they exploded far beneath us. However, the explosions were strong enough to push the sub sharply to the surface. Our Number One, Derek Anderson, flooded all the tanks with ballast as fast as he could, to keep us beneath the surface of the water, but it was no good. We had come up, and the Dornier returned to finish the job.

We lost both periscopes in that attack and barely managed to dive in time to avoid another run. Just before the periscopes went out of action, Commander Walters spotted two German anti-sub ships coming to join the attack.

With no periscopes and rocked by the bombardment of depth charges, we had no way of knowing their positions, so we couldn't hit them with our torpedoes. Firing torpedoes blind would only reveal our position to them. Commander Walters ordered the engines shut off and silence to be maintained. In the three hours since then no man had said a word.

We just sat deep beneath the waters of the North Sea and

waited while depth charges dropped. Some had been very near, the later ones further away. We were thinking the worst was over when…

KABOOOMMMMMMMMMMMMMMM!

An immense explosion rocked the sub. The air pressure began to soar as we sank deeper. We were now well beyond the water pressure this sub was designed to take. If we didn't get out of the dive soon the hull would collapse.

Suddenly the secondary lighting failed and we were plunged into complete darkness.

Damaged

As I sat there in the pitch black I thought: This is it. We're going to die.

"Start the engines," ordered Commander Walters. "Blow main ballast tanks."

There was no other choice. Below us lay only death; above us, at least, there was a chance of survival.

In the darkness we worked by touch and memory. A torch came on as the coxswain, Ian Bailey, found his feet. The engineers cursed as they tried to fire up the diesel engines, but the high level of carbon dioxide in the submarine had slowed down the starting process.

Meanwhile we struggled to vent the main ballast tanks by hand. We knew it would send telltale bubbles to the surface, but we hoped they'd be lost among the turbulence thrown up by the depth charges.

The hull of the submarine creaked and groaned under the pressure. At any second I expected the metal frame to give way and the sea to pour in.

Then the engines kicked into life.

"Take us up," snapped Commander Walters.

The hull of the *Sandtail* groaned and screamed as we

levelled out. The sound of air whistled through the sub as the ballast tanks emptied. Finally we were on an even keel again.

I checked the depth gauge, but it was out of action. The pressure of the sudden dive had been too much for it.

"Set course six zero five," ordered Walters.

All the time we waited for another explosion.

"I counted twenty-four," commented Chief Petty Officer Stannard.

We all knew what he meant. The smaller German ships usually carried ten depth charges each. That meant a total of twenty depth charges would have come down from them. The real question was, how many depth charges had the Dornier carried? Were there more to come? We were obviously lucky. No more explosions followed. The sea fell silent. And so leaking, battle-scarred and with no periscopes, we limped our way home.

For the last leg of the journey back to base at Montrose, on the east coast of Scotland, we sailed on the surface, with Commander Walters directing operations from the conning tower. The attack had smashed the periscopes and destroyed our wireless aerials, so under the surface we would have been helpless. We were a sorry sight. With water leaking in from cracks in the hull, it was obvious that the *Sandtail* would need an extensive refit before she could return to active service.

On the first night back on land, I was sitting in the quarters I shared with my friend, Jimmy Ferguson, the *Sandtail's* Third Officer, discussing what would happen to us now we were without a boat, when there was a knock at our door.

Jimmy opened it to reveal a motorbike messenger dressed in waterproofs and still wearing his goggles and leather helmet.

"Lieutenant Smith?" he asked.

"That's me," I said.

"Orders for you, sir."

I took the envelope from him and waited till he'd gone before opening it. It was an official-looking brown envelope with official-looking marks on it, but the message inside had been scribbled on a scrap of paper: Lieutenant John Smith to report to Inververgain Base, Loch Striven, 10th August.

Jimmy saw the puzzled frown on my face and grinned. "Let me guess: the Admiralty have promoted you to Captain?"

I handed him the scrap of paper. He read it and shrugged, obviously as puzzled as I was.

"Loch Striven," he mused. "Isn't that where those odd experiments are going on?"

"What odd experiments? Chemical weapons? I don't fancy being used as a guinea pig in any kind of experiment."

"No. Some peculiar sort of boat someone's invented. It's supposed to be a secret."

"If it's supposed to be a secret how do you know about it?" I asked.

"I've got an uncle who works on the River Clyde. He and his workmates saw some strange craft being put through its paces. Let's face it, a submarine – even a midget one – isn't something you can hide easily."

I was intrigued. "A midget submarine?"

"That's what Uncle Baxter thought it looked like. But then, Uncle Baxter also thinks he saw the monster in Loch Ness, so you have to take what he says with a pinch of salt." Jimmy grinned again. "Anyway, lucky you."

"Why lucky?" I asked.

"Well, you'll actually get to find out what's going on there and see what this mystery is all about. Who knows, the top brass might be trying to trap Nessie herself to use against the Germans. You might be going up there to catch the Loch Ness Monster!"

Old Friends

Two days later I arrived, as ordered, at Inververgain Base on Loch Striven on the Firth of Clyde. The first person I saw as I walked through the gates of the Base was an old friend from Naval College, Peter Redford. Like me, he was a Lieutenant who'd gone into submarines.

"John!" he greeted me cheerily. "Don't tell me they've roped you in on this as well?"

"Roped me in on what?" I asked.

Peter winked at me mysteriously.

"Top secret," he said. Then he laughed and added, "Except about half the population of the Firth of Clyde know about them because they look so peculiar, and no one thinks they will ever work properly."

"What are you talking about?" I asked. I hazarded a guess, remembering what Jimmy Ferguson had told me. "Midget submarines?"

Peter laughed again.

"See?" he chuckled. "Even you've heard about them. It shows just how secret they are! But don't worry, I'm sure the Germans won't be interested. Like I say, no one expects them to work. Not on long journeys anyway. Nothing further than

Glasgow. Anyway, come and have a cup of tea and you can tell me what's been happening to you since I last saw you. Lost any good submarines lately?"

I was curious to see these midget submarines that everyone seemed to know about and was tempted to ask Peter if he'd show me them, but instead I decided to join him in his offer of a chat over a cup of tea. It had been at least a year since I'd last seen him, and there's nothing that submariners like more than getting together and swapping stories about life beneath the waves.

I followed Peter along the quayside until we came to a group of battered old buildings. From one of them wafted the smell of tea brewing.

"This is it," said Peter. "The worst sandwiches and the lousiest tea in Britain. But when you're hungry and thirsty, it seems like manna from heaven."

We went in and found ourselves a table, and Peter brought us over a mug of tea each. He'd been right, the tea was awful. It was thick, brown and sludge-like. I shrugged in cheerful resignation as I sipped at it.

"I expect it's not their fault," I said. "It's the shortages caused by the war. They've had to use the cheapest sort of tea leaves."

"These aren't tea leaves, this is made from tea dust," said Peter. "This has nothing to do with the war. I bet you this place always made terrible sandwiches and awful tea. Well, how are you? I ran into Jerry Kent and he said you'd had a spot of bother. Lost your boat."

"Jerry is exaggerating, as he always did," I said. "We ran into problems out on the Norwegian coast, and as a result the *Sandtail*'s in for a refit. Nothing wrong with her that a bit of welding and a few coats of paint won't put right."

"And a couple of new periscopes, from what Jerry says," grinned Peter.

I shrugged.

"All right, there was some structural damage," I admitted. "But we got four German ships, so we didn't do too badly. How about you?"

Peter grinned and pushed back the lock of fair hair that fell across his eyes. It was a mannerism of his that he still had, one I remembered from when we were at Naval College. Even when he had his hair cut very short, he still put his hand up and pushed it back.

"Me?" said Peter. "Well, after we did our training I got a commission on the *Swallow*. Trim little craft, one of the S-types, but old."

"The *Swallow*?" I said. "I heard you were on the *Swordfish*."

Peter nodded.

"That was afterwards," he said. "After we were sunk in

the *Swallow*." He shook his head, and for once his usual cheerfulness went out of his face. "A bad business. We hit the bottom, way down. Lost eight men."

"What happened?" I asked.

"U-boat," said Peter. "Luckily for us it was on its own and not in a pack, or we'd all have bought it."

He shrugged airily, dismissing it.

"So, that was it. I was patched up back at base, and then sent out on the *Swordfish*. Where I was very happy, until I got the call to come up here."

"To the secret mission that's so top secret that half of Scotland knows about it," I commented sarcastically.

"Oh, the mission's secret enough," said Peter. "And believe me, I've been trying hard to find out what it is, but no one is saying anything. All we can guess is that it's to do with looking for something in the Scottish lochs. After all, I've seen these midgets subs, and I can't believe they can get very far under their own power."

I frowned. A thought had just come into my head.

"What's the matter?" asked Peter.

"I'm thinking about the Chariots," I told him. "You know, the human torpedoes. A bit larger than a torpedo with a couple of divers riding on it. Maybe this is another version?"

Peter thought about it for a moment, and then his face broke into a broad grin.

"Do you know, John, I think you may have hit it! It makes more sense than bringing experienced submarine officers all the way up here just to do some exploring locally. And if you are right, it means that we could be sent anywhere in the world."

I sipped the tea and thought about it seriously, and then suddenly the realization struck me.

"Not just anywhere, Peter," I said. "I think I know just where we're going."

"Where?" he asked, intrigued.

"A place where no one of this country's armed forces, not the Navy, not the Air Force, not the Army, nor the commandos, have been able to get to so far. I think we're being sent right into the lion's den."

"Where?" asked Peter again, still puzzled.

"The fjords of Norway," I said. "I think they're sending us to sink the *Tirpitz*."

Briefing

We assembled in the Briefing Room just before 0800 hours the next day. There were twenty of us, sitting at individual desks as if we were back at school. Apart from Peter, I knew just two of the others: Daniel Cartwright and Edgar Wood. They'd also been at Naval College with Peter and myself, although they had been a year ahead of us. The other sixteen men sitting quietly at their desks were a mixed bunch. A couple of them were in their early thirties, most were in their early to mid-twenties. I guessed that Peter and I, at twenty, were about the youngest in the room.

At 0800 on the dot, the door to the Briefing Room opened and the voice of the Number One snapped out "'Tenshun!"

We all sprang smartly to our feet as a small bearded figure strode into the room and took his place at the desk in front of us. This was Rear Admiral Pike.

"At ease," he said. "You may sit."

He surveyed us all for a second, and then said:

"You are all here because you volunteered for special services. It is time for that volunteering to be turned to good use."

The Rear Admiral unrolled a picture and tacked it to

the board. A buzz went round the room as we saw that the picture was of a very small submarine. What made it unusual was the lack of a conning tower. Instead it had a small hatch opening on the top.

"By now you will all have heard rumours about our new secret weapon, which means it is no longer a secret," he said wryly. "This, gentlemen, is the X-craft. A midget submarine that holds a crew of four men: the commander, navigator, engineer and a diver. You are those crews. Later your commanding officer will be allocating each of you to your various crafts. My task now is to inform you of your mission."

Pike moved over to a map of Europe tacked to the wall, and tapped the coast of Norway.

"Hidden in a fjord here is the German battleship *Tirpitz*."

At this Peter turned to me and winked. Pike saw this and snapped acidly: "Is there something the matter with your eye, Mr Redford?"

"No, sir," said Peter crisply.

"Then kindly pay attention."

I resisted the strong temptation to smile at Peter's being told off.

Pike moved away from the map and began to pace around in front of us.

"There is no need for me to tell you about the havoc that

Tirpitz is causing to our Navy in the North Sea. The RAF have tried bombing her, with no success. Last year we tried using a team of Chariots to mine her. Some of you were involved with that mission and I know how bitterly you felt its failure. Well this time there is going to be no failure. This time we are going to sink *Tirpitz*, and you are the men who are going to do it!"

I shot a quick look at the faces of the men around me. So some of them had been out there before? I looked forward to talking to them afterwards and getting the inside story on those "human torpedoes".

Pike continued the briefing.

"We are sending out five X-craft. Each one will be towed behind a regular S-class submarine. A caretaker skeleton crew of three will be in each X-craft on its outward journey to keep it operational. You gentlemen will have the luxury of being passengers on the S-sub on your way to Norway.

"Once the fleet are within range of the Norwegian coast, you will transfer to your crafts, and then carry out your mission.

"Because these craft are very small there has been no room for luxuries, such as wireless communications. Once you have set out in them you will not be able to communicate with each other, or with anyone else. You will be on your own."

Pike tapped the picture of the tiny sub.

"You have one periscope. That is your only contact with the outside world. That, and your diver, whose job it will be to cut a way through the anti-submarine nets that bar the way to the fjord.

"Each X-craft is armed with two 2-ton charges, each situated in a casing at either side of the sub. Your job is to place those charges beneath the *Tirpitz*. You will need to co-ordinate the timing for placing the charges so that you don't blow each other up."

He looked at his watch, and then announced: "The fine details of your mission will be given to you on your way to Norway. In the meantime, I suggest it is time that you get acquainted with your new craft." He looked at Number One, who was still standing stiffly to attention by the door. "Number One, give them their crew allocations and then take them out to see their new homes."

Number One took over at the front of the room and began to give us our crew allocations.

"The midget subs have been designated X5, X6, X7, X8 and X11," he announced.

"I wonder what happened to X9 and X10?" I whispered to Peter as Number One turned to a board and began writing our names on it in chalk.

"Sank due to mechanical problems, so I hear," Peter whispered back. "Apparently they've had a lot of teething troubles with these things."

We watched as our names went up.

Peter had been put in command of X5, and I was in charge of X11.

I felt a thrill as I saw my name go up as commander. Even though it was just a four-man boat, X11 was my very first command.

Number One got us five commanders to stand out front, and then called out the rest of our crews in turn to join us. My crew were: Eric Stevens, who was to be my navigator; James Munro, my engineer and pilot; and Bill Watson, who was to be our diver. There was no time for proper introductions at that time, merely a nod at each other as each man's name was called out and he stepped out to the front to join us.

"Right," announced Number One. "You've met each other. Now come along and meet your craft."

As I walked along the quayside with my crew I couldn't help feel a bit of a fraud. Here was I, twenty years old, and in command of men much older than me and much wiser in the ways of the sea.

Eric Stevens was Australian and about nine years older than me.

Short, stocky, tough, blond-haired. He'd once had a deep tan, but his time in submarines had led to it starting to fade. He was a cheery soul and even as we walked I could hear him telling a joke to our diver, Bill Watson. Watson was from Toronto, Canada. We were certainly an international crew on X11: one Englishman, one Australian, one Canadian, and a Scot.

"So the Germans caught these Prisoners-of-War escaping from this camp," said Stevens. "The Camp Kommandant lined them all up and told them: 'Vot you haff done is a serious crime against the Reich and you all deserve to be shot! However, I am a kind and gentle man, so instead I shall be sending you to ozzer camps! Half of you will be going to Poland, and ze ozzer half will be going to Germany!' The Kommandant paused, and then he added: 'The top half of you will be going to Poland, and the bottom half to Germany!'"

Watson joined in Steven's laughter as they walked along side by side. I noticed that the fourth member of our crew, James Munro, didn't join in. Munro was a tall red-haired Scot. Too tall, one would have thought, to have fitted comfortably inside a submarine. I moved alongside and fell into step with him.

"Stevens is a bundle of laughs, isn't he?" I commented.

"Some things shouldn't be laughed at, sir, if you want my opinion," replied Munro with a scowl. "People being killed by the Germans is one of them."

"I think Stevens is just trying to relieve the tension," I said, hoping to pour oil on troubled waters. The last thing I wanted was half of my crew at loggerheads with each other.

"Mebbe," said Munro. "Still, I don't think it's a thing to make jokes about. Some of us have lost friends and family in this war."

"I'm sure Stevens means no harm," I said. "After all, think how far he's come to fight this war. Halfway across the world. If he'd wanted I'm certain he could have stayed safely at home in Australia."

This time I'd said the right thing. Munro looked at Stevens as he chatted to Watson, and nodded.

"Aye," he said. "I never thought of it like that."

"I was just thinking about something that Rear Admiral Pike said back at the briefing," I said, trying to turn the conversation.

"Aye?" said Munro. "Which bit would that be, sir?"

"About the Chariots expedition last year," I said. "It seems some of our team were on it. Do you know who?"

Munro nodded, and once more the expression on his face hardened.

"Aye," he said. "I went out with my brother Robert on that mission." His face darkened with a mixture of sadness and anger as he added: "I came back. He didn't."

The X-Craft

I didn't ask Munro anything further about the failed Chariots mission. I was sure he would tell me all about it himself in his own good time.

By now we had reached the far end of the quay, and here in front of us were five of the smallest submarines I had ever seen. They looked almost like toys.

"There you are," announced Number One. "Climb aboard and take a look."

As commanding officer I was first to climb down the hatchway into X11. To call it a midget submarine was no exaggeration. The whole thing was about 50 feet long on the outside. There was no room to stand up anywhere inside the sub, let alone move from side to side easily. Inside, the pressure hull was about five and a half feet in diameter at its widest point. From there it tapered to either end, fore and aft. The deck was also raised six inches from the bottom, cramping the space even further.

The four of us stood pressed together, shoulders slumped in a stoop.

"My first act as commanding officer of this craft," I

announced, "is to order us all to sit down before we knock ourselves or each other out trying to move around."

We sat down at our stations in the tiny control room. My seat was at the periscope position, right in the centre. Stevens was acting as my first lieutenant and his place was just behind me at the hydroplane, pump and motor controls. Munro was in front of me at the steering. Watson sat where he could find a space near to the watertight door to the wet and dry room, or W & D room for short. This was between the cramped control room and the forward compartment. Once flooded, Watson would be able to open the hatch above and get out of the sub, when the time came for him to cut the anti-submarine nets.

The forward compartment itself was a tiny space which housed the fuel tanks and batteries. At the rear was the after compartment where the engine and the motor were kept.

At each side of the interior was a large lever. These levers opened the two outside bays, one each side of the hull, and dropped the explosive charges. The aim of our mission, according to Rear Admiral Pike, was to get close to *Tirpitz* and drop our charges beneath it, timed to go off with enough breathing space for us to get clear.

The four of us sat there, looking around the tiny sub. All of us had been in cramped submarine quarters before, but this X-craft was a whole new experience. It was like being in a sardine tin. We could all reach out from our respective positions and touch each other without stretching.

"Neat," commented Stevens. "Everything's here. And you don't have to walk around to get it. Very energy-saving."

"If the Germans pick these things up on their sonar they'll just think we're a shoal of fish!" grinned Watson.

I tested the periscope.

"Well, skipper?" asked Stevens. "What's the vision like?"

"After the periscopes I've been used to, this is like looking through the bottom of a beer bottle," I complained. "Still, as it's all we've got, it'll have to do."

"So long as it gets us to Norway," grunted Munro. "We'll finish the job from there."

For the next few days we tested the X-craft out, taking them up and down Loch Striven. The X-craft were slow. Their maximum speed on the surface was 6 knots, and about 5 submerged. Not that speed was that important on our mission. Operation Tirpitz was all about us being able to sneak our way past the German defences and get into the fjord where *Tirpitz* was berthed.

The night before we were due to set sail, I sat in the Officers Mess with Peter and the commanders of the three other X-craft: Daniel Cartwright, Edgar Wood, and an Australian, Stephen Pitcher. All of us joked about the lack of space inside the tiny experimental subs, and how there was no room inside them to stroke a cat, let alone swing one.

"The chaps I feel sorry for are the caretaker crews," commented Daniel, in between sipping his beer. "After all, we only have to spend a couple of days in them once we get to the Norwegian coast. Those poor chaps will be in them for over a week. Can you imagine?! A whole week cramped up in one of those things. Let's hope they all get on with each other."

"Maybe," murmured Stephen, "but there is one thing that no one's mentioned in all this."

"What's that?" asked Peter.

"Well," said Stephen, "we've all agreed these things aren't made for speed. They're also not made for long-distance travel, which is why they're being towed all the way across the Atlantic."

"Correct in every way," nodded Edgar. "Give that man a coconut."

"So the question that comes to my mind," continued Stephen, his eyes twinkling mischievously, "is … does anyone know how we get back?"

We all sat silent for a moment, and realized that it was the one question none of us had thought about.

"They're sure to keep the subs waiting for us," said Daniel confidently.

"Even if the Germans attack the submarine fleet once they realize what's going on?" mused Stephen. "Like after we've sunk the *Tirpitz*, for example?"

"They'll wait for us as long as they can," put in Edgar. "Of that I'm sure."

"So am I," said Peter confidently. With that he raised his glass in a toast. "To the sinking of *Tirpitz*!"

Setting Sail

At 0600 the next morning we set sail. Ahead of us was a journey of 1,500 miles across rough and icy seas full of potential dangers. Floating mines, packs of German U-boats, anti-submarine boats, enemy destroyers and aircraft laden with depth charges ready to bomb us as soon as they saw our shapes beneath the water.

We travelled in a convoy of five submarines. Myself and the rest of the crew of X11 were in the submarine *Saracen*. X11 itself, with its caretaker crew of three, was towed behind us on a long cable. Each X-craft had been trimmed down by the bows so that it followed about 40 feet below the depth of its parent submarine. In this way it was hoped that any enemy planes that spotted the larger subs wouldn't also spot the midgets.

As we travelled in the relative comfort of the *Saracen* I thought with sympathy of the crews on board the X-crafts. While the parent submarines travelled on the surface at night, the midgets had to keep submerged, only coming up every six hours or so to change the air.

It's a strange life, being in a submarine. All the things you take for granted on land become amazingly precious. Like air. The only oxygen in a submarine is the stuff that's there before you close the hatch. Once the hatch is shut, from that moment you begin to breathe less and less oxygen and more and more carbon dioxide. The longer you stay below the surface, the greater the percentage of carbon dioxide you breathe in. For that reason, most submarines remain on the surface as often as they can, only diving when necessary.

If the worst happens and the sub sinks and you can't get out, then all you breathe is carbon dioxide and you die of suffocation.

Fresh water is also very limited in a submarine. The first thing to go is washing. Not that it matters, because if no one in the crew washes, then after a while no one notices the smell of body odour. One sure way to disguise it is to never take your clothes off. So most of us submariners, when out on patrol, kept the same clothes on all the time, often for weeks on end. After a long patrol, whenever I arrive home for shore leave and finally take my clothes off, a layer of white powder falls off my body. This is dead skin.

Going to the toilet is another problem in a submarine. There are toilets, but often they don't work, and more than one submariner that I know had suffered the embarrassment of flushing a toilet under water, and being covered by the contents as they came back under pressure. As a result most submariners prefer a bucket which is then emptied out when the hatch is opened. The inside of a submarine that has been underwater for a long time is not a great place for someone with a delicate sense of smell.

On our second day out I was called to see Commander Perry, the commander of *Saracen* and the leader of this small fleet of submarines.

"Well, Lieutenant, it's time to co-ordinate the rest of the operation," Perry told me. "Your orders once you've left us." He opened a buff envelope and took out a sheet of paper. "At this same moment, the commanders of the other submarines in the flotilla are issuing these same orders to your fellow officers." He handed me the sheet of paper. It simply said: "T-time will be 0800 hours after embarkation. Rendezvous for return twelve hours later at 2000 hours."

"Thank you, sir," I said, handing it back to him.

I returned to the cramped and tiny quarters I shared with my fellow crewmen from X11 and filled them in on the instructions I'd just received.

"T-time is at 0800 after we leave the *Saracen*," I told them.

"Eight o'clock in the morning is breakfast time, not tea-time!" pointed out Stevens.

"Target time, idiot," grumbled Munro, but not with any spite. To my relief, he'd become quite used to Stevens's jokey manner in the time we'd spent together.

"I know that," grinned Stevens. "You know your trouble,

Scotty? You wouldn't know a joke if it came up to you and bit you in the ankle!"

"So we've got twelve hours to get in and dump the charges, and then another twelve to get out again," said Watson.

"That's right," I nodded. "All the other crews are getting the same instructions, so if we're not away from *Tirpitz* by eight o'clock on the morning of Target Day, we'll be among the casualties on the bottom of a Norwegian fjord."

"And getting back?" asked Stevens.

"2000 hours, twelve hours later," I said. "If we miss that, we miss the bus home."

We had been at sea for four days when we ran into trouble. We were on the surface, hatch open, along with the other four subs. Each, as usual, had its midget towed behind it beneath the surface. Today we were at the head of the flotilla.

I was standing in the conning tower along with Commander Perry, both of us rolling slightly with the movement of the sub as it moved forwards through the waves of the North Sea. We were scanning the sea ahead through our binoculars. Suddenly I spotted something on the horizon.

"Possible enemy due east, sir!" I said.

Commander Perry was already scanning through his glasses.

"Well spotted, Lieutenant!" he said.

There was no doubt about it, it was a wolf pack of German U-boats, running on the surface, just like us. I counted six conning towers.

Commander Perry scrambled down the ladder into the hull of the sub. I followed him and heard him give the order to close the hatch.

"Alert the others," Perry ordered his wireless operator. "Wolf pack on the horizon."

The crew moved to their stations, getting ready for action.

"Where do you want me and my crew, sir?" I asked Perry.

"You stay with me, Lieutenant, in case I need you," said Perry. "Assign your crew for'ard with the torpedo operators."

I hurried to our quarters to let Stevens, Munro and Watson know the situation. As I did, I squeezed past the wireless-operator and heard him reporting the situation to the rest of our small fleet.

"Enemy wolf pack approaching from east. Position latitude 63 degrees 3 degrees longitude. Six in number. All boats to action stations."

Stevens, Munro and Watson were all ready for action.

"What's happening, skipper?" asked Stevens.

"It looks like we're in for a fight," I said. "The Commander would rather avoid it and get us to Norway, but I don't think this lot are going to miss the opportunity for a scrap. Especially when they've got a one-sub advantage."

"Where does the Commander want us?" asked Watson.

"Helping the torpedo operators," I said.

"Suits me," said Munro. "Anything I can do to sink a few Jerries, count me in!"

My three crewmen hurried aft to the torpedo tubes, while I returned to midships. Commander Perry was standing with the radar operator watching the sonar of the approaching U-boats on the screen. It was hazy, but the blips were there all right, as were the other blips indicating our other four subs. Our companion subs had joined us now and we were strung out in a line, heading towards the six U-boats.

The initial noise of the submarine crew swinging into action had died down. Everyone was at their positions, waiting. The only sounds were the bleeping from the sonar and the occasional crackle from the wireless as the subs communicated with each other, updating enemy positions.

"Set Torpedo One for two and a half miles," Commander Perry said into the communication tube.

From the for'ard compartment we heard the clanking as a torpedo was loaded into Number One tube, set for two and a half miles, ready for firing.

"Range?" demanded the Commander.

"Three and a half miles and closing," said the sonar operator. "Three and a quarter. Three miles. Two and three quarter..."

"Ready…" ordered Perry.

"Two and a half…"

"Fire!" barked Commander Perry.

There was a hiss and our submarine recoiled in the water as our torpedo was discharged.

"Enemy torpedo incoming!" came a warning shout from the operator.

Sunk

"Alter course," shouted Perry. "Bearing five nine zero."

The command was passed along inside the hull. I felt the *Saracen* lurch as it turned sharply to port, then straighten on to an even keel, still heading for the U-boats. On the sonar screen we saw the German torpedo heading in our direction, but on a bearing that would take it past us.

The sonar showed that the leading U-boat had swung away slightly to avoid our torpedo, and the rest of the wolf pack had followed it. We were now almost level with the U-boats.

"Hard to port," ordered Perry, and the shout went down the lines of communication. "Hard to port."

The metal hull of the *Saracen* creaked under pressure as the engines were thrown into reverse and the flaps raised to bring us sharply round. The other four subs in our group had also begun to fan out so that all five of us moved behind the U-boats.

On the sonar we watched the German wolf pack separate and begin to turn.

The commander smiled grimly.

"Right," he said. "Lay two torpedoes ahead of the target in the eastern sector. Fire on my mark."

The inside of the submarine fell almost silent. The only sounds were the metal on metal of the two torpedoes being loaded into the tubes, and the bleep of the sonar.

We studied the sonar screen, watching our target turn away from the rest of the wolf pack. The Germans were obviously intent on picking us off one by one.

"Steady," called Perry, and the *Saracen* shuddered, the metal of the hull creaking as we slowed. "Bearing five three seven."

"Fire!" shouted Perry.

The *Saracen* rocked violently in the water as the two torpedoes rocketed from their tubes. The torpedoes clear, Perry ordered another shift in our course to take us away from our target.

On the sonar I spotted one of the U-boats moving into a position where it would be able to hit us.

"Sir!" I called.

Perry had already spotted it.

"Hard about," he said crisply.

"Hard about it is, sir," came the response.

Again the *Saracen* shuddered in the water, kicking against the abrupt change of forward motion. I dreaded to think what all this was doing to the crew in the X11. With no communications and given their size, the craft would be taking a terrible battering.

There was a sudden deafening noise as our torpedoes hit their target, blowing it up. There was no time for celebrations, however, because we were too busy trying to get away from the firing line of the other German subs.

Perry's order of "Hard about!" was just in time: another U-boat had fired its torpedoes straight at our forward position. All of us heard the terrifying sound of German torpedoes in the water, echoing inside the sub. We waited, motionless, holding our breath as the *Saracen* desperately banked, continuing its turn. There was a loud WOOOSH as the torpedoes just missed us.

We were overwhelmed by the sounds of explosions as torpedoes from other vessels hit, though whether it was our torpedoes hitting the U-boats or German torpedoes hitting our subs, we couldn't tell.

I tried to get a better idea of the situation from the sonar screen, but the noise had scrambled everything, fuzzing the screen. Then I saw movement: four blips heading away north.

Commander Perry rapped out an order to the wireless operator: "Regroup ten degrees south-south-east. Alert rest of flotilla."

"Regroup ten degrees south-south-east," repeated the wireless operator. "Copy?"

Back came the replies from the other submarines.

"Copy, *Snug*."

"Copy, *Scavenger*."

"Copy, *Siskin*."

I waited for the fifth and final signal: "Copy, *Sealy*." *Sealy* was the sub that was carrying Peter Redford and the crew of X5. There was silence amid the bubbling sounds of the sea outside.

The wireless operator looked questioningly at Commander Perry.

"Send out a signal to *Sealy* asking for confirmation," said Perry.

"*Saracen* to *Sealy*, did you receive last message?" the wireless operator said into his microphone.

There was no response.

"*Saracen* to *Sealy*," repeated the wireless operator. "Come in, please."

I looked at the sonar. The four blips that indicated the surviving German U-boats were now nearly off the screen as they made their escape. That left just four blips on the screen, grouped together: *Saracen, Snug, Scavenger* and *Siskin. Sealy* had vanished.

Norway

We continued our journey in a sombre mood. Four of the German U-boats had made their getaway, leaving two of their number on the bottom. Our losses had been the fewer, just the *Sealy* and the X5 midget sub, but we'd all lost good friends and we felt the emptiness of their loss. It was especially hard for me. I couldn't believe Peter Redford was dead. Gone – my old friend.

Once we were sure the Germans were out of range, our four surviving subs surfaced and with each submarine's commander in their conning towers, Commander Perry conducted a short service for our fallen comrades, saying just a few words to commend their bodies to the deep. Then we set sail again, making our way across the turbulent waters of the North Sea.

Although we'd lost one of the X-craft the mission would still go ahead, but now with four of us making *Tirpitz* our target instead of five.

For the next three days we proceeded in convoy, staying on the surface where possible, diving when danger threatened. We couldn't afford another battle in which more of the X-craft might be lost.

A few times, as we sailed just beneath the waves, one of the submarine commanders would spot a German tanker, or supply ship. Under normal circumstances we would have attacked and sunk it, but Commander Perry had been given express orders that our mission was too important to be jeopardized by an unnecessary attack that could bring us to the enemy's attention.

On the eighth day we reached Norwegian territorial waters. Though perhaps it would have been more accurate to call them "German-controlled Norwegian territorial waters", after the invasion in which the Nazis had taken control of Norway.

I was sitting in our quarters playing cards with Stevens, Munro and Watson, when a young rating arrived and interrupted our game.

"Lieutenant Smith," he said. "Compliments of the Commander, he needs to see you right at once."

I looked down at the hand I was holding. Four aces and the King of Hearts. It was the first decent hand I'd been dealt in two hours of playing.

"When the Commander says right away...?" I queried, tempted to delay my visit to Commander Perry until this hand had been played.

"He means right away, sir," said the rating.

With that he disappeared.

Stevens saw the look on my face and grinned.

"If I was a betting man, which I'm not," he said. "I'd say you had a hand that was sure to win this game, whatever any of the others of us is holding."

"And you could be right," I said ruefully, throwing my cards down on the box top we were using as a card table and getting up.

It was Munro who picked up my fallen cards as I left the tiny room. I heard him laugh out loud, and reflected that at least I'd cheered that usually unhappy Scot up and given him something to laugh about.

Commander Perry was waiting for me by the periscope. He stepped away from it as I approached.

"Take a look," he said.

I put my eyes to the periscope and looked. In front of me was a rugged coastline, a forbidding landscape of bleak high mountains broken up with deep crevasses.

"The Norwegian coast," announced Perry as I moved away from the periscope. "We've arrived. Time to transfer you to your X-craft."

We surfaced out of range of any coastal watchers. Then began the task of changing crews. We sent over a rubber dinghy from the *Saracen* to the X11 and the three men who'd been caretaking our midget submarine slid down from the deck of the tiny sub into it. Their relief at being out of the tiny craft was obvious. All three men looked pale. In fact it seemed to me, as we helped them on board the *Saracen*, that there was a bluey-green tinge to the sickly white pallor of their skin. Whether it was the high levels of carbon dioxide in the midget sub, or the rough crossing, I didn't have time to ask. Myself, Stevens, Munro and Watson were too busy getting into the dinghy for the return trip back to X11.

Just before I stepped down, Commander Perry stopped me.

"Officially your orders tell you to rendezvous here at 2000 hours tomorrow evening," he said. "However, German patrols permitting, we'll try and give you another few hours' grace. I'm sure that, if you manage to sink the *Tirpitz*, the Admiralty will have the decency to allow you that extra time, but we can't stay here indefinitely. After 2200 hours we will have to head for home."

I nodded.

"Understood, sir," I said.

With that I joined the other three in the dinghy, and we set out for our midget sub.

The inside of X11 seemed even smaller than I remembered it. It was also swimming with small pools of stagnant water.

"It stinks!" exclaimed Stevens.

"We're only going to be in this thing for just over 24 hours," I pointed out. "The poor blighters who've just left it spent eight days in here."

"Yeah, but I bet it didn't smell like this for the first few days of the journey," countered Watson.

We squashed into our places and made last-minute checks of the equipment. Everything seemed to be in working order. The caretaker crew had done a good job of maintaining her on the rough journey over.

I climbed the short ladder and took a last look out through the open hatch at the large subs that had brought us here, at the open sea, and at the Norwegian coast. The commanders of other three X-craft, X6, X7 and X8, were doing the same thing. From the decks of our tiny craft we saluted each other. Then I dropped back down the ladder and pulled the hatch cover shut.

"Take us down, engineer," I said.

"Aye aye, sir," said Munro.

The air hissed out of our tanks as ballast water filled it, and we began to dive.

We were now out of contact with all other human beings. Ahead of us were the icy waters of the channels that led to the fjords, floating mines, anti-submarine nets, batteries of German guns ... and *Tirpitz*.

Through the Minefield

According to our information, *Tirpitz* was in the safe harbour of Kaafjord, at the head of Altenfjord, twelve miles inland from the open sea. Various obstacles lay ahead of us before we could even get into Kaafjord itself. The first were the German minefields. Although they were anchored in certain areas of the fjord so as not to present a hazard to German shipping, we didn't know their exact location so they presented us with a serious danger.

The second was the amount of sea traffic passing up and down the long Altenfjord. Any one of them might spot us and relay information about our position to the German lookout posts, armed with heavy guns and depth charges, strung along the mountainous sides of the fjord.

If we got past those hazards, then we would come up against the boom across the entrance to Kaafjord. This boom was like a level crossing gate at a country railway crossing – a long arm that went across the entrance to the inner fjord, raised and lowered by the guardhouse soldiers on the quay. Beneath it hung a metal net, intended to stop any submarines from getting in.

If we managed to get past that, then the next obstacle was a layer of anti-torpedo netting surrounding the *Tirpitz*, suspended from floating buoys. This anti-torpedo netting was like chain-mail hanging down in the water. If we got tangled up in that then we'd be well and truly trapped.

Finally there were *Tirpitz*'s own defences: heavy and light guns, depth charges, backed up with sharp-eyed lookouts and sonar devices.

The seabed itself also presented a danger with its constantly changing depths of water. If we ran aground in the silt and shingle we could damage our craft. At worst, we could get stuck on the bottom and have to abandon ship, swimming out through the W & D room. For all of us on board X11, that was not an option because of the danger of being spotted. We couldn't afford to alert the Germans that an attack on the *Tirpitz* was taking place and foul things up for the others. So, if we got stuck on the seabed, then we'd just stay there until we heard an explosion that told us one of the other X-craft had been successful.

Our main problem in getting past all these obstacles was that we were trying to do it with limited instruments. Our only navigational aids were our periscope, our compass, and a constant check on our speed to help us estimate the distance we'd travelled. The rest, including our position in the fjord, was based on guesswork and keeping our senses alert. With no wireless, we also had no way of knowing how the other X-craft were doing.

We kept to fifty feet, making 4 knots, listening out for other craft.

"Was it like this before?" I asked Munro. "When you were here with the Chariots?"

Munro gave a bitter laugh.

"The nearest we got before was landing on the Norwegian coast," he said. "We lost the Chariots before we got to the fjord."

"What happened?" asked Watson.

And so, as we cruised silently along the long Altenfjord, Munro told his tale.

"There were four of us. Two men to each Chariot. We were on a Norwegian fishing boat, disguised as fishermen. The two Chariots were bolted to the bottom of the fishing boat, which slowed us down on our journey across the North Sea."

"You were lucky you weren't spotted by a German patrol," said Stevens.

"We were spotted," said Munro. "They picked us up in Norwegian waters. Luckily for us our Captain, a very brave Norwegian, persuaded them that we were just honest fisherman on our way back to Norway with fish for the brave German protectors.

"After that incident we thought we were home and dry. We'd made it one and a half thousand miles across freezing and rough seas, talked our way past an armed German patrol, all we had to do was disconnect the Chariots and get into Trondheim fjord, and that would be it. Bang would go the *Tirpitz*."

"What went wrong?" I asked.

"The bolts holding the Chariots to the bottom of the trawler failed," said Munro. "We lost the Chariots. Both of them. They came loose and sank right down to the bottom into a trench, too deep for us to recover them." He shrugged. "That was it. Mission abandoned. We daren't take a chance on going back by the same fishing trawler and getting picked up, so the Captain put us ashore and we made our way on foot across the mountains into Sweden." Munro fell silent for a moment, then he said: "The Germans caught up with us in the mountains. Ambushed us. Robbie, my brother, got shot. The rest of us managed to get away, into Sweden. And the Swedes got us back home."

Munro's story had an effect on all of us. We felt for him. To have got all that way, and to fail because of something as silly as some faulty bolts. Even Stevens didn't want to make a joke about it.

All the time Munro had been talking I was still keeping a close watch through the periscope. As he finished, through the dark waters, I suddenly saw something. There were cables ahead stretching up from the bed of the fjord. Mines!

"Slow ahead group down," I ordered.

"Slow ahead group down, sir," came the response from Munro.

"What is it, skipper?" asked Watson.

"A minefield," I said. "We must be getting near to the entrance to Kaafjord."

Above us were the German mines. Through the water I could see their spines reaching down towards us. One touch of our hull on the end of one of those metal probes and we'd be blown sky-high.

I gave instructions and slowly, very slowly, Stevens steered us first to the right, then to the left, as we wormed our way in and out through the forest of metal cables. Only a midget submarine could have manoeuvred through, anything larger would have snagged on a cable and brought the nearest floating mine down, and… Boom!!

After what seemed an eternity we cleared the last cable. We had done it – we were out of the minefield.

I checked my watch. 0300 hours. Five hours to go before we were due to sink the *Tirpitz*. All the twisting and turning to get through the minefield had made distance-judging difficult, but according to my calculations I guessed that we were approaching the boom that separated Altenfjord from Kaafjord.

"Periscope depth," I ordered.

"Periscope depth it is, sir."

Slowly we came up from our cruising depth of fifty feet.

"Stop motor," I said.

"Stop motor."

I looked through the periscope. In the early morning light I could just make out the boom arm across the entrance to Kaafjord. Our calculations had been correct.

"How's it look, skipper?" asked Watson.

"Looking good so far," I said. Then a movement on the surface caught my eye, and I moved the periscope slightly to the right to get a better view. It was a small coaster, just heading towards the entrance to Kaafjord. As I watched I saw the boom arm begin to rise, the wire netting beginning to emerge from the water.

"They're lifting the boom!" I exclaimed.

"What?!" said Munro, surprised.

"They're letting a coaster through! Right, let's see if we can slip in on its wake! Start motor! Full speed ahead. Take us down to just below periscope depth."

Munro opened the vents while Stevens set the course for the boom. All of us felt the agony of the X-craft's slow speed. Would we make it before the Germans brought the boom down? Had the other X-craft spotted the boom going up? Were they behind us? Was one of them already inside

Kaafjord? There were so many questions, and no way to find the answers. We were putting everything we could into willing X11 to go faster.

"Speed?" I asked impatiently.

"5 knots," replied Stevens.

"Can't you push it any faster?" I asked. "If we don't get to the entrance quickly, that boom will be down! And if we get caught in that wire netting…"

"Increasing speed," said Stevens. "Five and a quarter knots … five and a half…"

Already we could hear the metal of the X-craft groaning as Stevens pushed it faster, the engines starting to squeal in protest at being made to work harder than they were designed to. Six knots was possible on the surface, but against the pressure of the water…

"She won't last, skipper!" warned Munro urgently.

"OK, reduce speed," I ordered reluctantly. "But keep it as fast as you can…"

My words were cut off as a scraping sound echoed throughout the sub. The metal of the boom's netting! They'd lowered the boom!

"Slow ahead group down!" I yelled sharply. "Dead stop! Dive dive dive!"

The last thing we wanted was to get our propellors tangled up in the wire of the boom.

Munro and Stevens worked together, bringing X11 to a shuddering stop, and sending her down until we felt her scrape the bottom of the fjord.

"Stop motor!" I instructed.

With the motor cut off, we listened. Metal on metal. There was no doubt about it, we were caught in the boom's net.

Tragedy

"OK, Watson," I said. "You're on. Get us out of this."

"On my way, skipper," nodded Watson.

With Munro's help he pulled on his bulky diver's outfit, although it was a real struggle in the confines of the midget submarine. Once he was in his suit he pulled on his flippers, picked up his oxygen mask and goggles, then the huge pair of wire cutters.

"Right," he said. "Put me in the hatch."

Stevens opened the door to the wet and dry room and Watson hauled himself into the tiny cramped space. He then spun the huge wheel, sealing the door shut.

"All ready, skipper," he said.

"Shut number two main vent," I instructed.

"Number two main vent shut," nodded Munro as he opened the tanks to flood the W & D room.

"Shut number two Kingston," I ordered.

"Number two Kingston shut," said Munro as he turned the second valve. We could see the water level now rising through the tiny porthole in the door. Watson had his mask and goggles on now. He gave us a thumbs up sign as the water covered him. Then we heard the outside hatch open.

I went to the periscope. Through its lens I saw Watson swim out of the hatch and grab hold of the wire netting. It took Watson some time to cut away at the thick cabled wire.

When Watson thought he'd cut enough for us to get free, he swam back in through the hatch. We heard the outer hatch door shut, then a knock from inside the W & D room. Watson's hand appeared in the porthole, thumb raised.

"Open number two main vent," I ordered. "Open number two Kingston."

As before, Munro repeated each command as he opened the valves to drain the W & D room.

With the water gone, Munro spun the wheel to open the hatch and Watson scrambled back inside.

"I think there's enough room to get clear if we edge forward slowly, skipper," he said.

"Let's hope so," I said. "OK, Stevens. Start the motor. Then slow ahead group down."

Watson had done a good job. We moved forward, each movement brushing clear of the tangles of wire from the boom net.

"Right," I said. "We've made it into Kaafjord. Next stop, *Tirpitz!*"

I waited until I reckoned we were well past the boom at the entrance to the inner fjord, then gave the order to come up to just beneath the surface.

"Blow tube."

"Tube blown, sir."

I hoped that here, in the middle of the wide fjord, a tiny object such as our periscope top wouldn't be noticed by the shore batteries and that the guards' attention would be concentrated out towards Altenfjord rather than inside the boom.

I looked through the periscope, and there she was! About three miles away. *Tirpitz*. Even from this distance she looked gigantic! Suddenly there was a flicker of movement at the edge of the periscope lens. I turned towards it, and was confronted by the terrifying sight of a ship's bows bearing down on us.

"Crash dive! Dive dive dive!!!" I shouted urgently.

Munro and Stevens worked furiously, opening the ballast tanks and taking us on a new course.

As we went down we heard the hiss of air bubbles rush past outside and we were thrown violently about, our hull creaked ominously. We clearly heard the sound of the ship's propellers as it sailed overhead, missing us by what must have been barely inches.

"Phew!" said Watson wiping the sweat from his forehead. "That was a close one! Must have been a supply ship."

"Let's hope *Tirpitz* has got everything it wants for the next few hours," I said. "I don't fancy coming that close again!"

I checked my watch. 0530 hours. Just two and a half hours before target time. I wondered how the other midget subs were getting on.

"Slow speed ahead," I ordered.

"Slow speed ahead," nodded Stevens.

From here, according to the charts, the seabed began to rise. The last thing I wanted was to scrape the bottom and run aground, so steady ahead was the rule of the moment.

There was also the problem of the anti-torpedo nets that surrounded *Tirpitz*. They were another reason for proceeding at a cautionary speed; I didn't relish hitting them full on, even at just 5 knots.

"Steady as we go," I murmured.

"Steady as we go, sir," repeated Stevens.

Suddenly we heard the sound of an explosion echoing through the water. But it hadn't come from ahead of us, from the *Tirpitz*. It had come from behind.

We exchanged glances.

"It came from the other side of the boom, sir," said Munro. "From Altenfjord…"

"And that was more than just depth charges," muttered Watson angrily.

I nodded. The noise and the shock waves from the

explosion, even at this distance, meant that the charges of one of the other midget X-craft had blown up. Four tons of explosives. One of our small fleet had gone, and with it four of our comrades. I wondered which one it was? And what had caused it? Had the Germans spotted it and fired at it or depth charged it, causing its bombs to go off?

"They'll be looking for us now, sir," said Munro.

"Then we'd better get on and blow *Tirpitz* up before they find us," I said grimly.

Caught In The Nets

As the aftershocks of the massive explosion in Altenfjord died away behind us, we moved slowly forward through the water of Kaafjord on a course for *Tirpitz*. All the time we were aware that from now on the gunners on the massive German battleship would be watching out for any signs of enemy encroachment. Surfacing was now out of the question. From now on we had to inch along the bottom of the fjord, trying to avoid rocks, floating mines, anything that could damage our craft.

I kept my fingers crossed that the Germans would think the craft which had been destroyed in Altenfjord was the leader of the fleet and so would concentrate their search for other vessels in the waters of the outer fjord. If they did that, I could also only hope that the two remaining X-craft had made it through into Kaafjord.

"Still steady as we go, sir," whispered Stevens.

"Keep it that way," I murmured back.

We had to talk quietly now, in case the Germans were listening with hydrophones.

"I calculate we should be nearing the anti-torpedo nets now, sir," whispered Munro.

I kept my eyes pressed against the eyepieces of the periscope.

"Got them," I said.

I could see dimly through the waters, the tight small meshed metal netting, draping down like a curtain in front of us.

"Slow ahead group down," I ordered.

"Slow ahead group down," repeated Stevens.

"Stop motor."

Again, the less noise going through the water that might give away our position, the better.

Through the periscope I could see there was a gap between the bottom of the netting and the bed of the fjord of about four feet. Too low for us to go under without getting caught up in it.

Cutting through a net with such a small mesh would lose us too much time. We also had to be careful not to move the net too much in case we disturbed the buoys floating on the surface. Following the explosion, I was sure that the lookouts on *Tirpitz* would be scanning the surface waters of the fjord, and any sudden bobbing about by the buoys that held the anti-torpedo nets would alert the lookouts to our presence and lead to a major attack on us. Stealth was the only way to get our two 2-ton charges to the *Tirpitz*.

"OK, Watson," I said quietly. "Time for you to go back

into action. There is a chance that we can scrape through, but we need another two feet above us to get clearance without drawing attention to ourselves. Cut a line about a foot up from the bottom of the net. Then I want you to see if you can lift it enough for us to slide under."

"I'll do my best, skipper," nodded Watson.

Once again he pulled on his thick rubber suit, oxygen mask and flippers. Then, taking his cutters with him, he crawled into the W & D room and we went through the procedure to flood it so that Watson could swim out.

As before, through the tiny porthole we watched the W & D room fill with water, then the hatch opened, and I turned my full attention to the periscope eyepiece and watched Watson swim out towards the anti-torpedo net.

Watson swam to the bottom of the net and began to cut. The work was harder this time because of the smaller mesh. There was also the added danger of Watson accidentally pulling on the net as he cut, causing the buoys on the surface to be pulled under. If that happened then we were as good as dead.

Cutting the net was a painfully slow process. The tension inside the X-craft as we waited was almost unbelievable. In the silence I could hear the blood pounding in my head.

Three inches. Four. Five. Carefully, painstakingly, Watson cut upwards. Six inches. Seven. Eight.

I could feel Munro's and Stevens's eyes on me as I kept watch on Watson through the periscope, waiting for me to let them know what was going on. Was Watson succeeding?

"Nearly there," I whispered to them.

Nine inches. Ten. Eleven. Watson made one final cut to give me the twelve inch line I'd asked for. Then he turned towards the periscope and gave me a thumbs up.

"Start up motor," I ordered quietly.

The motor hummed back into life.

"Right, dead slow ahead," I murmured quietly to Stevens. "And I do mean dead slow. I want us to just slide through this. But if we do get caught, then I want to be able to stop at once, I don't want to pull the netting along with us and bring the buoys down."

"Dead slow it is, sir," said Stevens.

The craft moved forward very slowly.

"Keep her down," I ordered Munro. "Scrape the bottom if necessary, but keep her down as low as she'll go."

"Keeping her low, sir," nodded Munro.

Through the periscope I saw Watson take hold of the anti-torpedo net and swim upwards, taking the netting with him. I knew he daren't take it up too much because of the disturbance it would cause on the surface, but I had calculated that all I needed was that extra foot and we could hopefully slide through under it.

"Steady as she goes," I murmured.

I was aiming at the point in the net where Watson had made his cut, and hoping that we were low enough that our periscope would slide through the cut.

As we moved forward, Watson floated into view, blotting out the periscope. Then we were under him.

There was a scraping sound outside, metal on metal. The netting was scraping on our hull.

Stevens and Munro looked at me, questioning.

"Still steady," I murmured.

I could feel myself sweating. I'd taken us beyond the point of no return. We were now at that crucial halfway point where the net was draped on top of us. If we attempted to reverse now, we'd be trapped, caught up in the metal mesh.

From beneath us there was an ominous groaning and a scraping sound.

"Our hull's on the bottom, sir," reported Munro. "Take her up?"

Like me, beads of sweat had appeared on his face.

If I took her up, then I was sure we'd get caught in the net. If I didn't take her up, then here was a chance that we'd damage ourselves on the rocks on the bed of the fjord, or we could run aground in the shingle. My decision now really would be life-or-death.

Tirpitz!

I made my decision.

"We're staying down," I said. "Keep her steady. And let's hope Watson can get that net up high enough to sneak us under."

Slowly, ever so slowly, we moved forward, inch by inch. At any second I expected us to lurch to a sudden halt as we snagged on either the net or the seabed, but we continued to slide slowly forward. Then the scraping of metal from the nets on our hull stopped. We had made it.

"OK, take us up three feet," I ordered. "No more, we daren't risk being spotted."

"Decreasing depth by three feet," said Munro.

Meanwhile Watson had returned.

"That was a tight one!" he gasped as soon as he took off his face mask. "I don't know how we're going to get under going back."

"One step at a time," I said. "First, we have to deal with *Tirpitz*."

I looked at my watch. It was now 0710. Fifty minutes to explosion time.

"Did you see any sign of the others while you were out there, Watson?" I asked.

"I'm not sure, sir," said Watson. "The water's fairly thick with all the silt that's been churned up from the bottom. I think I saw something that could have been one of ours in the distance, but I didn't want to swim over and investigate in case it wasn't."

"Did you get a look at *Tirpitz*?" I asked.

"Two hundreds yards to starboard," replied Watson. "You can't miss it. Her hull is nearly touching the bottom of the fjord."

"Good," I said. "Then let's get there and drop our cargoes."

I went to the periscope, at the same time ordering Stevens to change course 40 degrees to starboard.

We came about, and there she was. Even through the silt that clouded the waters, there was no mistaking her.

"OK," I said. "Take us in, dead ahead. And steady as she goes. We don't want to bang into her, not with four tons of explosives on board. It may sink *Tirpitz* all right, but I'd rather we made it home in one piece."

As we moved slowly forward towards the hull of the giant German battleship, I couldn't help but think of our comrades who hadn't made it, who'd been blown up just a couple of hours ago, so near to their target, yet so far.

We were now almost beneath the enormous hull.

"Arm cargoes," I ordered. "Set for forty minutes."

Munro set the timers on both of our 2-ton explosive charges.

"Cargoes armed, sir," he said, when he was ready.

"Drop cargoes," I ordered.

We heard a very dull thud as the two huge bombs rolled out and settled into the silt.

"Cargo one away, sir," reported Munro.

"Cargo two away, sir," echoed Stevens.

"Right," I said. "We've got just over thirty-five minutes before they go off. Let's get out of here!"

As we turned, I caught a glimpse through the periscope of something in the water about two hundred yards away, further along *Tirpitz*'s hull. It was another X-craft!

I grinned broadly and told the others: "We're not alone, boys! Someone else has got through. I guess they've just managed to drop their charges as well. That means there are now at least eight tons due to go off. We'd better take a chance and put some distance between us and the explosion. Full speed."

"Full speed it is, sir!" responded Stevens.

I kept a close eye on my watch all the way back to the anti-torpedo netting, watching the minutes tick away.

As I saw the netting ahead I gave the order: "Slow ahead group down."

"Slow ahead group down, sir," repeated Munro.

The X-craft slowed in the water and then came to rest with its nose touching the netting.

"Right, Watson," I said. "Out you go again. Lift that thing and get us back under it."

"Shall I cut it again, sir?" he asked.

As he asked, there was a sudden muffled explosion from the direction of *Tirpitz*. Then another.

"Depth charges!" exclaimed Stevens.

"They must have spotted the other X-craft!" I said with horror.

Target!

The explosions continued behind us as the depth charges dropped down around our sister X-craft.

"Quick, Watson!" I ordered. "Get out there. Don't waste time cutting anything, just pull up that net and let's get under it! We'll take a chance on the buoys moving. With a bit of luck the surface waters will be boiling so much from their depth charges the Germans won't notice."

While Stevens kept us on course and I kept watch through the periscope, Munro once more helped Watson into the W & D room. It was all done at speed; there was no time to be lost. The minutes to the explosion were still ticking away: 27, 26, 25, 24... And from behind us the sound of depth charges going off still reverberated through the water.

It seemed to take for ever, but at last the W & D room filled with water and the outer hatch opened. Watson swam out towards the anti-torpedo netting. He moved upwards, hauling the net with him. Although the water helped reduce the weight of the metal mesh, it was still very heavy.

"Take her to 2 knots," I ordered. "Keep her low."

Stevens and Munro worked feverishly at their controls to

keep X11 on a straight and level course, despite being rocked by aftershocks coming through the water.

We moved under the net, our hull scraping on the bed of the fjord.

Instinctively I checked my watch. 20 minutes before the blast. 19. 18. 17.

There was a terrible metallic crash from outside as the net became too much for Watson and it dropped on to the top of the craft. For a second I was worried that it would get tangled up in our propeller … but then we were clear.

"Right, get Watson back in double-quick!" I snapped.

Munro was already at the door of the W & D room, watching for Watson's raised thumb to appear to let us know he was in and the outer hatch was shut.

"He's in, skipper!" he reported.

"Good. Open number 2 vents and Kingston and get that door open!"

A few moments later Watson was back inside, being helped off with his wetsuit. He was panting with exhaustion.

"Right, full speed ahead!" I ordered.

"Full speed ahead it is, skipper!" said Stevens.

My watch now showed 11 minutes to detonation. I wondered what had happened to the crew of the X-craft that had been depth charged. And what about the third midget sub? Was that in the Kaafjord with us?

10 minutes to go. 9. 8.

The depth-charging behind us had stopped. Did that mean the Germans would now widen their search and come looking for us?

I checked our course. We were headed back out towards Altenfjord.

"Maintain 5 knots," I said.

"5 knots it is, sir," came the response.

Five minutes to go. Four. Three.

Through the cloudy water I could just make out the large mesh of the boom that separated us from the waters of Altenfjord, and beyond that the Atlantic. The boom was firmly down, keeping us trapped inside Kaafjord. I guessed that even as we were trying to get away, German reinforcement boats were on their way to scour the fjord for other midget submarines.

My watch showed 1 minute to go ... then zero ... and nothing happened. The charges had failed to detonate!

My three crewmen had been studying their watches as well, and looks of despair crossed their faces. Especially Munro, who'd come on this mission in memory of his brother, and now saw it turning to disaster.

"What d'you reckon's gone wrong, skipper?" asked Stevens.

I sighed heavily.

"It seems—" I began.

And then there was the sound of a terrific explosion way back behind us, followed by another, and then another. Our midget submarine was hurled through the water. We fought to right her again, desperate to keep her from going into the anti-submarine net beneath the boom.

As Munro, Stevens and Watson cheered and shook hands with each other, I said: "Looks like we've done it. Now all we have to do is get away."

Running Out Of Oxygen

With our mission accomplished, our objective now was to get out of the fjords and make the rendezvous with the *Saracen*.

Once more Bill Watson went out with the cutters and cut the bottom part of the boom netting, and soon had enough of the net open for us to be able to slip under. As before, it was a tight squeeze and only a midget submarine could have done it. I guessed most of the German attention was on the *Tirpitz*. If we'd damaged her as badly as I hoped we had, then all available hands would be busy picking up survivors.

We slipped through under the boom back out into Altenfjord, and Watson joined us back inside the sub.

"Right," I ordered. "Back out to the open sea! Course 543."

"Course 543 it is, sir," repeated Stevens.

By now the air in the midget sub was starting to get a bit thick. It had been many hours since we'd had a chance to surface and open the hatch to get some fresh air in. The build-up of carbon dioxide would begin to get to us soon, and there was a serious danger of us making mistakes. I was aware that all four of us were beginning to pant heavily, one of the first signs that we had begun to run out of oxygen. We were now mainly breathing in carbon dioxide. Unless we surfaced soon the next stage would be dizziness, then drowsiness, and finally sleep. A sleep from which we wouldn't wake up.

Stevens was already showing signs of drowsiness, his eyelids were drooping and I noticed his head kept jerking up as he fought to keep himself awake.

For myself, I could feel a fog starting to cloud my brain. It was becoming difficult to keep my eyes focused.

Bill Watson was the least affected, mainly because he'd recently been taking in oxygen while he was swimming outside.

"Watson," I said, "how much oxygen is left in your tank?"

Watson checked.

"About enough for just one more dive, skipper," he said.

I weighed it up. If we shared the oxygen around now then it would all be gone, and if we ran into nets or underwater obstacles, there'd be no way of getting past them because we'd have no diver.

On the other hand, we had the floating minefield in Altenfjord to get through. If we attempted to do it while we were in a dazed state, then there was every likelihood that we'd hit the detonating spines and blow ourselves up.

Our third option was to surface now and open the hatch. But if we did that, with the amount of German activity in the immediate area, we'd be caught for sure.

I reached my decision.

"We're going to pass round Watson's oxygen mask," I said. "Don't breathe too deeply all at once. Two shallow breaths each at first. Then we'll pass it round again. Hopefully it will keep our heads clear until we're through the minefield. After that, we'll surface as soon as we can."

I took in my breaths slowly and carefully. The fuzziness in my head began to clear almost at once. The others also seemed to become that little bit more alert.

After that first session, we passed it round amongst us again.

Watson took the last turn, and then checked the level of oxygen left.

"There's maybe enough for one person to have another shot," he announced. "But not enough for me to go out again."

"OK, let's hope we don't have to stay under any longer than we need," I said.

During all this we had been drifting slightly, as Stevens kept a loose touch on the navigation.

I had decided to set our return course through the minefield. It was dangerous, but it would give us cover.

I looked through the periscope, and saw again the forest of cables that anchored the floating mines, dead ahead of us.

"Right," I said. "Steady as we go."

"Steady as we go, sir," echoed Stevens.

Coming through the minefield had been difficult enough on our journey up through Altenfjord. Now, even after the shot of oxygen, we were still all feeling a bit light-headed. I had to fight to concentrate as I looked through the periscope and gave instructions to Stevens.

"Ten degrees starboard," I murmured.

He changed our course just enough for us to slip in between two cables. We were in shallow water now and I could see the detonating tips of the mines above us. They seemed even closer to us than on our journey inland. If I hadn't been suffering from lack of oxygen I would have made the connection much sooner. Of course! The tide! On this return journey the water level was lower than it had been on our way in!

"Depth?" I asked.

"Twenty feet, sir," said Munro.

Twenty feet! We had come up on a shelf rising in the middle of the fjord. I could see the long tips of the mines barely inches above us. If we even just so much as scraped one, we'd be dead.

"Keep her steady," I said. "Five degrees to port."

We scrambled along the seabed.

"Depth?" I asked.

"Nineteen feet, sir," responded Munro.

We were rising, forced up by the ebbing tide. Any second now and we'd be right up there, among the mines. I wondered whether I should change my mind, try and get us out of the minefield, but the forest of cables was all around us. It was one thing to try and maintain course due ahead, snaking with slight deviations as we went. It would be quite another to attempt to turn through 90 degrees. Surrounded by cables, we'd be bound to snag on one, and pull a mine down on us. It looked as if we were stuck, with no way forward and no way back.

Going Down For The Last Time

"Keep her steady," I murmured.

Inside the midget submarine all that could be heard was the hum of our motor, and our breathing as we made our way slowly forward.

"Depth?" I asked again.

"Still nineteen feet, sir," replied Munro. Then… "No, twenty. Twenty-two. Twenty-four."

He looked up as his face broke into a grin of relief.

"We've passed the shelf, sir!" he said. "We're going down!"

Once we had cleared the minefield I waited until we were far enough along Altenfjord to a place where I felt it might be safe to surface. I ordered us up to periscope depth and took a careful check around.

This far away from Kaafjord the area seemed clear. There were no boats visible on the water. At either side of the fjord were sheer cliffs, and there seemed to be no obvious German artillery positions on them.

"OK, blow tube," I ordered.

"Tube blown, sir," said Munro.

We rose to the surface.

"Careful as you open the hatch," I warned.

We all knew of cases where the hatch had been opened too quickly and the build-up of carbon dioxide inside a sub had led to it exploding out, hurling the man who'd opened the hatch out of the submarine.

The smell of fresh oxygen was the sweetest smell we could have experienced.

"Let's savour this fresh air for ten minutes, and then we'll be on our way," I said.

Over the next few minutes we all took turns to feel the fresh air and the sun on our faces, and then it was time to close up and submerge again.

I was now aware that we were running seriously behind schedule. As we neared the entrance from Altenfjord to the open North Atlantic it was almost 2000 hours already, the time scheduled for our rendezvous, and I calculated that we still had at least another three hours' journey time. Commander Perry had promised he would give us until 2200 hours, and then he would have to leave. At this rate we would arrive one hour too late. However, we had no choice but to push on and hope that the fleet might give us a bit more leeway.

At 2215 hours we were still three miles short.

"We're going to miss them," moaned Watson in desperation. "All this way and we're going to miss them!"

"We're going to be stuck if we do," said Munro. "We can hardly sail this thing across the North Sea. For one thing, we haven't got enough fuel to travel more than another twenty miles past the pick-up point."

"In which case we'll just have to sit and wait until the Germans arrive and pick us up," I said.

"If they do pick us up," commented Stevens. "After what we did to *Tirpitz* they're more likely to bomb us than pick us up."

"Let's take a chance and travel on the surface," I said. "We'll be able to go faster and we might still catch them."

"Unless they've gone already," pointed out Watson. "They were only supposed to wait for us until 2000. We're already two hours late."

"True," I said. "But we've got nothing to lose. Take her up."

Once on the surface I opened the hatch and scanned the sea ahead through my binoculars. Nothing. There was no sign of any of our fleet. It was possible they were still submerged, but without a radio we couldn't even signal our position.

"Full speed ahead," I ordered. "Let's keep our fingers crossed."

"Full speed ahead it is, skipper," said Stevens.

And so we sailed across that vast open expanse, our tiny craft heading into the open North Sea.

Through my binoculars I looked for any sign of the fleet. The moon was full and I could see for miles. Nothing.

Suddenly I heard the drone of a plane's engine behind me. I turned, and looked as the sound of the engine drew closer. My heart sank. Coming towards us was a Dornier bomber, unmistakable in the moonlit sky.

Hastily I dropped back down inside the midget sub and slammed the hatch shut.

"What is it, skipper?" asked Stevens.

"We've got company!" I shouted. "A German bomber. Dive!"

Munro and Watson swung into action, opening the valves and filling our tanks with ballast while Stevens kept watch on the controls and I took my position at the periscope.

The first depth charges exploded in the sea around us just as we were going down.

Unfortunately for us, out here in the moonlit waters, the Dornier had a perfect sighting of us.

Our hull creaked and groaned, and then suddenly water began to pour in from above the periscope housing.

"Our hull's been breached!" shouted Munro.

More water appeared, cascading down on to the main switchboard. Almost instantly sparks flew off the control panel and it caught alight, electrical fires breaking out, light arcing from the wires. Smoke began to fill the inside of the sub. We were now up to our knees in water and sinking fast.

We had only one choice and that was to abandon ship. And we had to do it quickly before X11 went down, taking us with her.

"Take her up!" I ordered. "Better to take our chances with the Germans than drown!"

As we reached the surface, the water was waist deep. The smoke choked and blinded us. I fumbled for the hatch and just as I was about to lose consciousness I somehow found the opening and managed to get the hatch open. I hauled myself out on to the tiny deck. Watson followed me, then Munro, then Stevens.

With no proper room, we clung to the metal and tried to get a foothold to stop ourselves from falling into the sea. With the heavy clothing we wore to protect us from the cold, we'd sink like stones if we fell in.

I couldn't see because of the waves and spray from the sea around us. I heard the rattle of machine-gun fire, and tensed, expecting the bullets to tear into us at any second. Instead there was a sudden dull WHOOOMPF from above. As I looked up I saw one of the Dornier's wings burst into flames. For a second it hung in the sky. Then it fell towards the sea on our port side in a cloud of smoke and flame.

"There!" shouted Munro, pointing.

I turned, and saw the shape of a submarine on the surface about half a mile away to starboard, the machine gun on its deck still pointing upwards in the spray. As I watched another rose from beneath the sea, its conning tower breaking through the waves. The *Saracen*!

Beneath us X11 was sinking fast. The sea was now up to our waists.

Just before our tiny craft went down, Commander Perry's craft pulled alongside us and we scrambled on to it, doing our best to get a grip on the slippery wet metal of the submarine's hull. Eager hands grabbed us, and hauled us aboard.

Once down below, Commander Perry shook each of us by the hand.

"Well done, all of you," he said. "According to our initial intelligence, the *Tirpitz* has had it."

"Just now we thought we'd had it too, sir," I said.

"To be honest, we'd just about given you up," Perry said. "Luckily for you we picked up the Dornier depth-charging something, and we knew it had to be you, so we came back."

"What about the other X-craft, sir?" I asked. "Any news of them?"

Perry's face grew grave.

"As far as we know, I'm afraid you're the only ones who made it back," he said. "If they were lucky, the Germans will have taken them prisoner. If not…"

He left the sentence unfinished. We all understood. That was war.

"Go on," said Perry. "Get yourselves a hot drink and something to eat, and bunk yourselves down. It's a long way home."

AUTHOR'S NOTE:

Although this is a fictional story, it is based on real events, but the names have been changed.

In the actual attack on *Tirpitz*, six midget submarines set out from Scotland for Norway, each towed by a large parent submarine. They were X5, X6, X7, X8, X9, and X10. Their crew lists were as follows:

X5 (towed by *Thrasher* – Commanding officer Lt A R Hezlet).

Operation crew: Commanding officer: H Henty-Creer

Crew: T J Nelson

D J Malcolm

R J Mortiboys

Passage crew: Commanding officer: J H Terry-Lloyd

Crew: B W Element

N Garrity

X6 (towed by *Truculent* – Commanding officer R L Alexander).

Operation crew: Commanding officer: D Cameron

Crew: J T Lorimer

R H Kendall

E Goddard

Passage crew: Commanding officer: A Wilson

Crew: J J McGregor

W Oxley

X7 (towed by *Stubborn* – Commanding officer A A Duff).

    Operation crew: Commanding officer: B C G Place

    Crew: L B C Whittam

    R Aitken

    W M Whitley

    Passage crew: Commanding officer: P H Philip

    Crew: J Magennis

    F Luck

X8 (towed by *Sea Nymph* – Commanding officer J P H Oakley).

    Operation crew: Commanding officer: B M McFarlane

    Crew: W Y Marsden

    R X Hindmarsh

    J B Murray

    Passage crew: Commanding officer: J Smart

    Crew: W H Pomeroy

    J G Robinson

X9 (towed by *Syrtis* – Commanding officer M H Jupp).
    Operation crew: Commanding officer: T L Martin
    Crew: J Brooks
    V Coles
    M Shean
    Passage crew: Commanding officer: E A Kearon
    Crew: A H Harte
    G H Hollis

X10 (towed by *Sceptre* – Commanding officer I S McIntosh).
    Operation crew: Commanding officer: K R Hudspeth
    Crew: B Enzer
    G G Harding
    L Tilley
    Passage crew: Commanding officer: E V Page
    Crew: J Fishleigh
    A Brookes

X8 and X9 were lost at sea on the outward journey. The four surviving midget subs that reached Norway were: X5 under Lt. Henty-Creer, X6 under Lt D Cameron; X7 under Lt B C G Place, and X10 under an Australian Reserve officer, Lt K R Hudspeth.

X10 suffered major electrical failures as well as serious leaks and had to abandon its part in the attack. It was able to make the rendezvous with one of the parent submarines and began its journey back to Scotland. However, because of gales, it was scuttled before it reached base.

X6 managed to penetrate the nets and place its charges, but was then spotted and attacked, and had to be scuttled. Cameron and his crew were taken on board the *Tirpitz* as prisoners.

X7 became entangled in the nets protecting *Tirpitz*, came under fire and sank. Only Lt Place and the diver survived and they were also taken prisoner.

X5 was subjected to a barrage from German armaments and disappeared. No trace of X5 or her four-man crew was ever found.

THE SINKING OF TIRPITZ AND AFTER

The *Tirpitz* was not sunk by the explosive charges laid beneath it by the X-craft, but was very badly damaged. All of the battleship's three main turbines were disabled, as were its generators, electric equipment, port rudder, and range-finders. The huge crippled ship lay out of action in the Norwegian fjord for six months while the German engineers worked to repair her. This gave the RAF time to plan their final assault on the ship, and on April 3rd 1944 a force of carrier-based aircraft attacked the *Tirpitz*. This attack caused such serious damage that she was unable to be repaired so far from a fully-equipped shipyard. *Tirpitz* was then moved south to Tromsø to be used as a floating coastal battery. While at Tromsø, *Tirpitz* was finally sunk on 15th September 1944 by a force of Lancaster bombers using 12,000 lb Tallboy bombs.

THE SIGNIFICANCE OF THE X-CRAFT ATTACK ON THE TIRPITZ

Tirpitz being put out of action by the X-craft had a threefold effect:

The vital supply convoys from Britain to Russia could continue in greater safety.

The sinking of *Tirpitz* ended the idea of the German Navy being invincible and in control of the North Sea.

The British naval fleet were released to engage the enemy in other theatres of the War, instead of being restricted to the North Sea as a protection against the threat of *Tirpitz*.

BRITISH AND GERMAN SUBMARINES OF WORLD WAR 2

BRITISH "S" CLASS SUBMARINES

Standard surface displacement: 715 tons
Overall length: 217 feet
Maximum beam: 23 feet 9 inches
Surface speed: 14.5 knots
Underwater speed: 10 knots
Range at 10 knots: 6,000 miles
Torpedo tubes: 6 bow; 1 stern
Reload torpedoes: 6
Guns: 1 x 3"; 1 x 20 mm AA
Diving depth: 300-350 feet
Crew: 44

The original "S" class subs in the early 1930s had six bow torpedo tubes and six reload torpedoes. These "S" class were designed for patrol work in the North Sea. Their standard surface displacement was 670 tons. After the outbreak of World War 2 a new "S" class was produced, heavier at 715 tons, and with the addition of a single torpedo tube at the stern. The S-class subs, however, were slow when compared with the German submarines, having a surface speed of just 14 knots against the faster U-boats' 29 knots.

BRITISH "T" CLASS SUBMARINES

Standard surface displacement: 1,090 tons
Overall length: 275 feet
Maximum beam: 26 feet 7 inches
Surface speed: 15.25 knots
Underwater speed: 8.5 knots
Range at 10 knots: 8,000 miles
Torpedo tubes: 10 bow (later versions: 8 bow; 3 stern)
Reload torpedoes: 6
Guns: 1 x 4"; 1 x 20 mm AA
Diving depth: 300 feet
Crew: 46-61

The "T"-class submarine was built to replace the "O" and "P" class subs which had suffered many technical problems, most notably a tendency to leak oil from their external tanks. The "T"-class subs had one major advantage over their predecessors: a bow salvo of ten torpedoes: six tubes opened from the forward end of the pressure hull, two from the casing above, and a further two faced forward under a raised deck at mid-length. In theory this gave the "T"-class the most powerful forward battery of any submarine in the world. However, in practice, the four external tubes could not be reloaded at sea. Also, the bulge of the deck casing needed to accommodate the forward external tubes caused a very visible bow wave at periscope depth. To try to overcome these problems, changes were made to later versions of the "T"-class subs, but these changes added to the already existing problem of drag, which made the underwater speed of the "T" class very slow Only 50 of the "T"-class subs were built.

BRITISH "U" CLASS SUBMARINES

Standard surface displacement: 540 tons
Overall length: 197 feet
Maximum beam: 16 feet
Surface speed: 11.25 knots
Underwater speed: 9 knots
Range at 10 knots: 3,800 miles
Torpedo tubes: 4 bow
Reload torpedoes: 4
Guns: 1 x 3"
Diving depth: 200 feet
Crew: 31

"U"-class subs were originally designed as unarmed boats to train surface forces in anti-submarine action. With the prospect of war they were equipped with the additions of four internal and two external bow torpedo tubes. Unfortunately, the bulbous casing needed for these additions led to problems: when a full salvo was fired the boat invariably surfaced. As a result, after trials with the first three such equipped boats, the external tubes were omitted. However, it was found that the bulbous casing still caused problems at periscope depth, and later versions therefore were made without a raised bow. These later versions of the "U"-class subs were much easier to handle.

BRITISH X-CRAFT (MIDGET SUBMARINES)

Standard surface displacement: 30 tons
Overall length: 51 feet
Maximum beam: 5 feet 6 inches
Surface speed: 6 knots
Underwater speed: 5 knots
Crew: 4

The X-craft were midget submarines and were based on a prototype developed privately by a retired submariner, Commander Cromwell Varley on the Hamble River in Hampshire. The X-craft were submarines in miniature, but without conning tower or torpedo tubes. Instead they had side-cargoes either side which contained time-fused high explosive charges. They were very cramped indeed. Unlike the faster (although slightly larger) Japanese Type A midget submarines, the X-craft had a diesel engine for surface cruising and recharging batteries, and an electric motor for submerged running. The X-craft were designed as weapons of stealth: to penetrate enemy harbours.

GERMAN U-BOAT TYPE VII (1940)

Standard surface displacement: 760 tons
Overall length: 220 feet 2 inches
Maximum beam: 20 feet 4 inches
Surface speed: 17 knots
Underwater speed: 7.5 knots
Range at 10 knots: 8,500 miles
Torpedo tubes: 4 bow, 1 stern
Reload torpedoes: 9
Guns: 1 x 3.5"; 2 x 20 mm
Diving depth: 400 feet
Crew: 44

The VII was one of two German submarines based on the First World War U-boat (the other was the smaller Type II at 250 tons). The major modification of both of these new U-boats over the original was the reduction in the size of the conning tower to reduce the silhouette on the surface. The Type VII was not intended for direct battle but for blockading action against warships. The Type VII played a major part in the battles in the Atlantic and North Sea against Allied merchant shipping.

As with all U-boats, the Zeiss fixed-height binoculars and periscopes were far superior to those of other navies, giving the U-boats an advantage in optical sighting, and therefore torpedo control.

GERMAN U-BOAT TYPE IXA

Standard surface displacement: 1,032 tons
Overall length: 251 feet
Maximum beam: 21 feet 4 inches
Surface speed: 18 knots
Underwater speed: 7.5 knots
Range at 10 knots: 11,500 miles
Torpedo tubes: 4 bow, 2 stern
Reload torpedoes: 16
Guns: 1 x 4.1"; 1 x 37 mm
Diving depth: 400 feet
Crew: 48

Although the IXA-type U-boats were larger and had a longer range than the smaller Type VII, they took a longer time to dive. They also could not go so deep and were more susceptible to damage.

However, as with all U-boats, the IXA had a faster firing process than the submarines of other navies and could fire up to five torpedoes at five separate targets within a few seconds.

GERMAN U-BOAT TYPE IXD2 (1942)

Standard surface displacement: 1,616 tons
Overall length: 287 feet 6 inches
Maximum beam: 24 feet 7 inches
Surface speed: 19 knots
Underwater speed: 7 knots
Range at 10 knots: 31,500 miles
Torpedo tubes: 4 bow, 2 stern
Reload torpedoes: 16
Guns: 1 x 4.1"; 1 x 37 mm
Diving depth: 400 feet
Crew: 48

The IXD2 was a larger and faster version of the IXA, but also with the same problems of all the IX types: namely taking a longer time to dive, and also unable to go so deep as the VIIs. However, along with most other types of U-boat, the superior pressure hull construction meant it was better able to withstand depth charge attacks.

THE GERMAN BATTLESHIP *TIRPITZ*

Displacement: 42,900 tons
Dimensions:

> Overall length: 791 feet
> Overall breadth: 118 feet 3 inches

Speed: 29 knots
Armament: 8 x 15" (4 x 2) guns
12 x 5.9" guns
16 x 4.1" AA guns
16 x 37 mm AA guns
16 x 20 mm AA guns
48 x machine guns
8 x 21 TT

4 aircraft

Crew: 1,500 (of which 103 were officers — including ship's surgeons and midshipmen)

Along with its sister ship, *Bismarck*, the *Tirpitz* was one of the two giants of the German Navy. In January 1942 she sailed from Wilhlemshaven to Norway, and it was in Norway that this giant battleship spent her entire career. In fact *Tirpitz* never took part in any actual surface action, but instead stayed securely in the

Norwegian fjords as a constant threat to the Allied Arctic convoys. This threat meant that large numbers of destroyers from the British Navy were kept on alert just in case *Tirpitz* ventured out of the fjords. As a result of this the Allied convoys were weakly protected, usually with six escorts, sometimes less, usually small Corvettes that hadn't got the speed to combat surface U-boats.

ISLAND OF FEAR

THE WAR IN THE PACIFIC

By December 1941 the Second World War had been going on for over two years, with Germany dominating a mostly occupied Europe, supported by its allies, Italy and Japan. During that time the United States of America had remained neutral. Then, in December 1941, without prior warning, Japanese fighter planes attacked the American fleet at Pearl Harbour on the island of Hawaii. It was an act that brought the USA into the War.

Although America committed many of its forces to the War in Europe and North Africa, it was the Japanese who were seen as the main enemy. As a result, a large part of the American war effort was in the Pacific.

By mid-1944, following the successful D-Day landings in Europe, Italy had surrendered and Germany was on the defensive. Japanese forces had dug in on many of the Pacific Islands and it seemed impossible to remove them. And as long as these islands were held by the Japanese they formed a solid ring of defence around the Japanese homeland.

So far the US had tried bombing the Japanese defences, both from battleships and from planes, but they had been impregnable to such attacks. If the Japanese were to be overcome there was only one way to do it – by putting Marines ashore on the beaches of the islands and taking them one by one. It was a deadly strategy, not least for the men who would be sent in to try and take these islands. The key island was Iwo Jima, but before any attack could even be considered, first the outlying islands had to be taken – the Marianas: the islands of Saipan, Tinian and Guam.

In June 1944 the US Marines set out to do just that.

Attack on Saipan

The noise of the battle was deafening. Gun and mortar fire from the Japanese defences poured down on us. Around me, Marines fell and crumpled on the soft sand of the beach as the enemy fire took its toll. The bombardment from our own ships lying off shore continued, the crashing of our bombs and rockets as they struck shaking the ground beneath me, as if earthquake after earthquake was hitting the island.

I'm John Smith of the 23rd Marines, 18 years old, and this was my first real experience of combat. Months of training at Boot Camp and lectures from our instructors had done their best to prepare us, but that had all been just practice. This was the real thing. This was win or die.

We'd hit the beach of Saipan at 0855. As we'd run from our LVT and dived for what little cover the beach had to offer, the Japanese had opened up from their defensive positions, and now we were pinned down. I struggled hard to keep down the sense of fear that threatened to overcome me. I kept muttering to myself, "You can survive this! You can survive this!"

Bullets smacked into the sand around me. We began to dig in, making holes in the sand as cover. Digging in is a hard enough thing to do at the best of times, but even harder when you're lying face-down, aware that if you put your head up too high a bullet could hit you. I was lucky, I'd managed to get behind a ridge of raised sand that gave me some cover, not much though.

I looked over at my buddy, Paddy Riley, who was also lying as flat as he could behind a ridge of sand. He gave me a big wink as if to say, "Don't worry, buddy. We can get out of this."

But then, that was the way that Paddy had. Paddy was big in every way: the way he looked, the way he thought, the way he acted. He seemed to have the attitude that he could brush aside any obstacle he came across. He was over six feet tall and broad shouldered. Paddy was very fit, and very fast for someone of his size. With his jet-black hair cropped short, Marine style, his broken nose slightly askew (a reminder of his days as a boxer back in civilian life), and his cheerful grin, Paddy was a tonic. When things looked bad, Paddy could always be counted on to cheer you up.

This first wave of our assault on Saipan had begun at 0700 hours, 15 June 1944. Although, in reality, the actual attack had started some time before. For the last four days our aircraft carriers and battleships had kept up a steady bombardment of the island of Saipan, pounding it with shells and rockets, trying to knock out the enemy defences.

They'd done their best, but the Japanese had had years to build really solid pillboxes and anti-boat gun emplacements.

This morning, at 0730, we'd begun debarking into our LVTs, our Landing Vehicle Tracked, also known as an amphtrac, or amphibious tractor. The aim had been for our LVTs to come right up out of the sea and on to the beach, and then go right up to the Japanese positions, under covering fire of our aircraft and battleships. The first problem had been the Japanese firing at us we came in to the shore. The nearer we got to shore, the closer their shells came to hitting us. Some of the LVTs did get hit. I saw two go down near us, Marines tumbling out into the water and sinking beneath the waves, loaded down with the weight of their packs.

Even the shells that missed us swamped our landing craft with water that rose up in huge great geysers as the enemy shells exploded in the sea around us.

As we neared the actual beach, we hit the coral reef. Our LVT managed to find a passageway through the reef and keep going for the beach. Others weren't so lucky. Some got stuck on the reef, and made a sitting target for the Japanese fire. As our vehicle came up out of the water on to the beach itself we took a hit that tore off our caterpillar tracks and our craft ground to a shuddering halt.

"Hit the beach!" Sergeant Sykes had shouted, and we had

done just that, running and ducking and dodging, bullets flying all around us.

Eight thousand Marines had set out in this first wave. Thinking of the casualties lying spread on the beach, and out there on the reef and floating in the water, I wondered just how many of us had made it this far.

"Smith! Riley!"

I turned my head and saw Sgt Sykes crawling as fast as he could through the soft sand towards Paddy and me.

"Sir?" I responded.

Sykes was a guy I had a lot of time for. Put some guys in command and they seem to forget what it was like being an ordinary soldier. Not Sykes. As tough as they come, but fair. Short in stature, his cropped hair was already grey, even though he was in his early thirties.

Sykes reached us and gestured with his thumb at a point high up ahead of us.

"There's a sniper up there, holed up in a pillbox," he said. "He's got himself well dug in. I need two men to go up there and take him out."

"Sounds like we're the two men, Sarge," grinned Paddy. "Me and John."

I felt a sick feeling deep in my stomach as Paddy said the words. That was the main problem I had with Paddy. Because he didn't seem to feel fear the same way as I did, he thought that other men didn't feel it either. For Paddy being in battle was excitement and adventure. For me, it was fear of being killed or badly wounded.

"That's what I thought," nodded Sykes. "I'm going to open a barrage of fire from over there behind the ridge." He indicated a point about a hundred yards away. "With a bit of luck that might blind-side him and keep him occupied enough to give you time to get up there. At least near enough to get some grenades in. The fact is, fellas, if we don't take that guy out, we're stuck on this beach and ain't going nowhere."

"Leave it to us, Sarge," I said.

Although my words sounded brave, I hoped any trembles in my voice didn't give me away. Like I said, I was scared. Luck had kept me alive this far. Now the ridge of sand between me and the enemy was my protection. In a few seconds Paddy and I would be coming out from behind that ridge of sand and making for that pillbox.

"Go when we start our diversionary fire," Sgt Sykes said.

"Yes, sir," Paddy and I nodded.

With that, Sykes turned and crawled back to join another group of Marines further along the beach.

"Looks like we get to be heroes," smiled Paddy.

I swallowed, doing my best not to show him how scared I was. I liked Paddy a lot. Out of all the guys in the platoon he was the one I'd describe as my best pal. It was a pity, from my point of view, he just had this desire to get into wherever was the hottest point of any battle. Still, as one old soldier had told us: "You can run and hide all you like, but if the bullet's got your name on it, you're gonna get it."

I forced a grin back at Paddy.

"Someone's got to be heroes, might as well be us," I replied.

We lay there, rifles ready, our attention now on Sykes as he reached the other group of Marines. The deafening noise of battle meant we had no way of hearing what he was saying to them, but the nods from the Marines and the cocking of their guns told us that this was our moment.

Sykes looked towards us and gave us a thumbs up. I swallowed hard and uttered a silent prayer to myself as I signalled back to him.

Sykes issued his instructions, and the Marines began firing blindly over the ridge, up towards where the sniper was holed up.

"That's us!" said Paddy. "Here goes nothing!" And he darted off.

Doing my best to hold back my feeling of fear, I followed him, trying to avoid the sniper's bullets, keeping my head low. Above us I could see the concrete pillbox set into the ground. A rifle poked through one of the slits and was firing.

Paddy stumbled and slipped, falling on to the sand. He struggled to get back up. I reached him, and then passed him, my teeth clenched tight shut with determination. As I scrambled up I pulled a hand grenade from my pack with my free hand. I was nearing the pillbox now. I could see the vertical openings, with long grass hanging down to conceal them.

Suddenly a rifle poked through the dark slit above me, and my blood froze. A rushing noise filled my ears as my heart began to pound. I tore the pin from the grenade and pulled back my arm to hurl it. I heard a CRACK! and felt a blow just above the elbow. The grenade was torn from my hand and hurtled away, heading back down the slope. I struggled to retain my balance in the shifting sand, desperately trying to pull another grenade out. Then I felt an explosion in my chest and I slumped to my knees in agony. Then I was falling falling falling falling...

Hit

When I came to I was back on the beach. A corpsman was bending over me, tying a huge dressing to my chest with bandages.

I opened my mouth, trying to ask him how I was, but no words came out. My whole mouth felt like it was stuffed with cotton wool.

The corpsman became aware that I was awake. "Save your breath from talking, kid. You're gonna need all you've got for breathing," he grunted.

An explosion rocked the ground beneath me and sent a shower of sand raining down on us. The corpsman ducked his head to keep the sand out his eyes, then carried on bandaging me.

"As soon as we can we're gonna get you off this beach," he told me. "Right now you're safer here. We try and haul you out, you're gonna die for sure."

I was dimly aware of him tying off the bandage, then there was another huge explosion and everything around me was blotted out again.

The rest of what happened was just a haze. Every now and then I floated back into consciousness to make out a change in what was going on. At one time I felt myself being carried and heard the splash of water around me. Then I was rocking backwards and forwards. All the while I was aware of a dull pain in my chest and my right arm that now and then seemed to fill my whole body with agony.

When I finally came round it seemed as if the whole room was going up and up. Then my head cleared and I realized the room really was going up and down. I was on a boat.

I tried to focus my eyes and get my bearings through the fog that filled my brain. I was in the medical quarters of our troop ship. I'd been in them before, but only for the occasional small wound, nothing serious. Now I as bandaged up like an Egyptian mummy. Drip tubes connected my body to bottles suspended by the side of my bed.

"He's awake!" came a voice nearby.

I tried to turn my head to see who it was, but a pain came up through my neck as I did so.

"Easy, John boy!" came a familiar voice.

Then Paddy Riley came into view, a broad grin on his face. His left arm was in plaster from shoulder to wrist.

"Paddy," I managed to say. "I saw you go down. I thought you were dead."

Paddy shook his head with an apologetic grin.

"Not me," he said ruefully. "Just plain clumsy. I slipped on that volcanic ash they call sand. Man, that's treacherous stuff! A guy can't get a footing on stuff like that."

I gestured at the plaster on his arm. He shrugged.

"I got this later. After I took out the pillbox."

I struggled to remember. It was all vague. The concrete pillbox. Me, running up towards it. The barrel of the rifle poking out straight at me.

"When you went down I thought you was a goner for sure," continued Paddy. "Anyway, I upped and let 'em have two grenades right through those holes. That did it! Took out the two of them in that pillbox. But it was thanks to you, going for them in the first place."

I could feel a muzziness in my head. There was so much I wanted to ask Paddy. What had happened to the other members of our platoon? Had we won? Was the island ours? What about the other Marianas islands? But everything was swimming out of focus again. I was slipping back into sleep. Back ... into...

Hospital Ship

It was a few more days before I was fully conscious enough to find out the whole story. Apparently my wooziness hadn't been caused by my injury, but by the drugs the medical corps had pumped into me to keep me under.

This time, when Paddy came visiting, I was able to act and talk more sensibly.

"You took a bullet in the chest," Paddy told me. "Lucky for you it was on the right hand side. They had to patch your lung up. If it had been on the other side they'd have been trying to put your heart back together. So, you've got a few cracked ribs, smashed collarbone, and a big hole in your back where the bullet came out."

"How do you know all this?" I asked.

"I bribed the corpsman to let me look at your file," grinned Paddy. "I told him I needed to know if my buddy was gonna die so I could fix up a collection for the funeral before all the other guys got split up."

I chuckled. It hurt, but at least I was alive. I felt an overwhelming sense of relief. I'd been in battle for the first time. I'd been wounded, but I'd survived. I was still alive!

"What happened after I got hit?" I asked.

"We did good," said Paddy. "The Top Brass are very impressed. Once again, the Marines are winning the war for Uncle Sam."

"Forget all that, just give me the details," I said impatiently. "Like, how long have I been here?"

"OK," nodded Paddy. "Five days, is the answer to that one."

"And the enemy?"

"On the run," replied Paddy. "Not that there are many places to run on that island. Trust me, Saipan is as good as ours. Word is we're gonna finish it, then take the rest of the Marianas. Tinian and Guam. Then it's full speed for Tokyo." He patted the plaster on his arm. "I just hope this is working before that. After all this, I'd sure hate to miss the Big One."

In fact it took a little longer for the conquest of the Marianas than Paddy anticipated. I lay in my sick bed and watched the days being ticked off the calendar and listened to the reports coming back to the boat from the combat troops. Over the next few weeks, from bits of conversation with other soldiers, scraps of reports from the medical orderlies, I pieced the picture together as I followed the action from my hospital bed. It turned out that after that first assault, it was another ten days, 25th June, before the main peak on Saipan, Mount Tapotchu, was captured. It was nearly another two weeks, 7th July, before the island was finally won by our boys. In the campaign to take Saipan, the Japanese lost 26,000 men. We lost 3,500 dead and 13,000 wounded. Including me.

As the days went by I lay in my bed in the floating hospital and watched as more and more men came in, wounded or dying. I was getting stronger by the day, and I knew that sooner or later some MO was gonna kick me out of bed and back to a bunk, because they needed the space for all the new casualties.

For me, it was a time of mixed feelings. As I watched the wounded come in, a part of me wanted to be out there, helping them try and win this war. But there was also that part of me that wanted to get out of this war alive, and I had to admit that part of me felt relieved that I was safe on the hospital ship and out of combat.

Finally, by the end of July, word came through that Tinian had also been taken and the Marines were now setting their sights on the third island, Guam. By now reinforcement ships had arrived and our hospital ship was stood down and headed back home. All men with "less serious" wounds were transferred to the ships that were staying, so that they could be patched up and returned to battle. These "walking wounded" included Paddy, whose arm was almost healed, so we said goodbye and he headed off back into battle. Me, I was still counted as among those who needed to return to the good old US of A for a full recovery. I still had a hole in my chest, a hole in my back, and a right lung that sounded like a leaky bellows if I breathed too hard. But I was alive. Eighteen-year-old Combat Marine John Smith. And I was going home.

Stateside

It took a while for us to travel back to the States. Once we were back at Camp it took more weeks of briefings and debriefings and medical checks before the MOs decided it would be cheaper and less of a problem for the Marine Corps if I did my convalescing at my parents' home in Kalamazoo, Michigan.

Kalamazoo is a small kind of town. It's a long stretch of railway track with single-storey houses and low buildings stretching alongside the track on either side. One way the track goes to Chicago, the other way leads to New York. Those are the two places most people on those trains go to. Very few people get off the train in Kalamazoo unless they've got business there.

Kalamazoo, like most American towns, is full of families who came from somewhere else. English, Irish, German, Scots, Dutch.

Mom and Pop lived in a little clapboard house on the outskirts of the town, out towards Comstock. Just around the corner from them lived my father's parents, Otto and Gretel Smith. My father's name is Charles, although he'd been christened Karl. My grandparents had changed his first name the same time they'd changed their own surname from Krupp to Smith. Yes, we Smiths were actually Germans.

Lots of Germans kept their German names. My Grandpappy, Otto, however, decided that his family were going to have a proper *American* name. So he chose Smith. Which, I'm told, is English.

Still, it's a nice simple name with no troubled connections. And that's what Grandpappy Otto was looking for in 1916.

Early at the start of the century, he and my grandmother had come over to America to settle and start a new life. With them they brought their son, young Karl. My pop. The Krupp family.

Then, in 1914 War broke out in Europe. Germany against everybody else. In 1916 the USA came into the War and Germany became America's most bitter enemy. Rather than let his family suffer because of their German name, Grandpappy Otto took drastic action. No more Krupp. From that moment on we were the Smith family.

We weren't the only ones. Lots of German families did this. Even the British Royal family did it. Up till the First World War their family name had been Saxe-Coburg-Gotha. So the British Royal family changed it and became instead the House of Windsor.

To an outsider it may seem strange. Here we were, fighting a war against the Japanese, the Germans and the Italians. Yet our combat troops were made up of men from Italian and German families as well as Irish, Dutch, English, and so on. No Japanese, though. The Japanese in America were still seen as a security risk by the Government. But the Germans and Italians had been in the country for a couple of hundred years.

Anyway, I got off the train at Kalamazoo and took a cab home.

"John!" squealed my mom when she saw me coming up the path. I just had time to remind her that I was still convalescing before she managed to hug me. My mom's got a tough kind of hug.

Within minutes of my arrival home, word had spread and half the neighbourhood started calling. To listen to my mom talk to them as she handed round cakes and coffee, anyone would have thought I'd taken the whole Marianas islands single-handed.

For the next few weeks I rested and recovered in Kalamazoo. Everything seemed just like it had before I went off to join the Marines. The only sour note for me was when Mom came home one day from the store with our groceries, and chattily said: "I ran into Mrs Pelt today. Her son Henry's home on leave. He's in the Marines now, just like you."

I could imagine Mom proudly telling Mrs Pelt how brave her son John was, and how I'd been injured.

"Do you remember when you were both at school and he got you into trouble for fighting?" Mom continued. "At least he's turned out well now."

I didn't answer her. Mom is the kind of person who will always try to find something good to say about someone. For me, Henry Pelt had always been a stupid bonehead.

Henry and I were opposites in almost every way. When we were at school he was a sports jock, built like a brick wall even when he was young, the star of all the sports teams. Me, I was kinda shortish and I preferred reading to sports. I don't think Henry ever read a book. Not for pleasure, anyway. I was good at Math and English and all that kind of stuff. Henry wasn't, but he wanted to be because his dad wanted him to be.

Henry was jealous of me because I got high marks in class, especially in Math, and he was nearly always near the bottom. Henry took it out on me the only way he knew how – physically. But though I was small I was also fast. After a scrap between us in the schoolyard, which Henry had started, but in which I'd given as good as I got, Henry decided it wasn't worth getting a bloody nose from me every time. Also, it didn't look good, a big sports jock like him getting punched in the nose by a bookworm like me. So, he tried a different way to have a go at me. When news started to come through from Europe about what was going on in Germany, Henry had his new weapon.

It was no secret that our family had once been called Krupp and came from Germany. My Grandmom Gretel still spoke English with a thick German accent. However, it did hurt me to find out what Hitler was doing in the name of Germans. We still had family back there in Germany. Cousins who would be fighting for Hitler. That also worried me.

But getting back to Henry, he started calling me "The Nazi".

Now most people, you ignore them and they shut up because it gets boring to have a go at people with no reaction. But not Henry. Henry didn't have the greatest brain in the world. For some reason he started to get it into his head that we'd changed our name from Krupp to Smith for more sinister reasons, because we were German spies. And had been since World War I.

At first I laughed at this. Then, when he started to spread it around his pals in Kalamazoo, it annoyed me. As a result, in about 1940, when we were both 15, we had a fight over it in the schoolyard after I called him out on it. This time I was so angry and I really let him have it. As a result I got into trouble. Henry's parents complained to the school principal. Our two families stopped talking to each other.

Time passed – we both left school. The War overseas continued, and then in December 1941, after the Japanese attack on Pearl Harbour, America came into the War.

As soon as I could, I joined up. Henry Pelt became a distant memory. One of those annoying figures from your past. And then he came back into it. As a Marine.

Henry Pelt

I was at the railway station, catching the train back to base camp. I'd persuaded Mom and Pop – and Granpop Otto and Grammy Gretel – that tearful farewells didn't go with a soldier-hero son, so I'd been able to get them to leave me at the station on my own to wait for the train. I was strolling along the platform when I saw Henry Pelt.

He looked bigger than ever. Very muscular. He saw me and hesitated, and I could almost see his brain ticking over, wondering what to say. Or whether to say anything at all. I decided that, as we were both wearing the same uniform it was ridiculous to ignore one another. So I nodded at him and said simply, "Henry."

He nodded back, curtly, but I could tell that the animosity was still there. It was in his eyes, the way he looked at me.

We stood there in silence, waiting for the train. Then he suddenly sneered and said, "Don't you find it strange, fighting your own people?"

I could feel the old anger welling up in me. After all these years, Henry was still playing the same stupid game. I did my best to hide my anger. Instead I simply shrugged and said, "That's the first I knew we were Japanese."

Henry scowled, then he snapped: "You know what I mean. We're fighting the Nazis. Your people."

"My people ain't Nazis, Henry," I responded coolly. "We're Germans. That ain't the same thing." With a twinkle in my eye, I added: "Remember, the Commander of the Fifth Marines is called General Schmidt. Sounds German to me. You saying a Marine Commander is a Nazi?"

Henry glared at me. He was always easy to beat in an argument if it required thought. He scowled.

"You think you're clever," he snapped. "You don't fool me. Your family changed their name trying to pretend they're not who they are. That makes you Nazi spies in my book."

"Which book's that, Henry?" I asked innocently. "You taken to reading lately?"

Henry's fists clenched and I thought for a moment he was going to hit me. Then he unclenched them. He wasn't that stupid. He wouldn't want to get into trouble for attacking another Marine in public. Especially one who'd just come back from the Marianas a hero.

"One day," he snarled, "you and me are gonna settle this once and for all."

"Suits me, Henry," I said. "Reading books at ten paces?"

Henry shut up and just glared at me. His brain couldn't work out an answer to that one.

Just then there was a loud whistling from the distance. Our train was on its way in. I was going back to the War, and I could once again forget about Henry Pelt.

Briefing Two

In fact it was many hours before I could even begin to forget about Henry Pelt. Not only were we on the same long train journey, we also caught the same bus from the station back to Camp. We didn't speak again the whole trip. Nor even exchange looks. It was as if we just wanted the other one gone from our lives.

Me, I felt angry. Before, Henry's accusations had just been born out of ignorance. Now, with the evidence in front of him, that I'd been in combat and nearly died for our country, America, for him to keep going on about me and my family being "enemy Nazis" was so stupid it made my blood boil.

Luckily for me, Henry and his idiotic attitude began to vanish from my mind almost as soon as I got back among my old buddies. It was good to see them again, especially Paddy, who looked even fitter than he did before we launched our attack on Saipan.

"Hey, John!" called Paddy delightedly when I walked into the barrack room. "How you doing?"

Just the sight of him with the same old lopsided grin and the warm welcome on his face made me feel good.

"Fine, Paddy," I said. "Got some good old Michigan air in

my lungs and just loafed around eating my mom's cooking. Just what the doctor ordered. What's been happening here? How's the War going at the front line?"

"Things are hotting up," said Paddy, with a pleased wink. "Something big."

"Oh?" I asked. "What is it?"

"Dunno," said Paddy. "Maybe we're gonna attack Tokyo itself. Whatever it is, it's definitely cooking. The Top Brass have been gathering and there've been lots of top level meetings! I feel it in my bones, John! This is the big one!"

As it turned out, Paddy was almost right. It wasn't the big one itself, Tokyo, but it was the next thing to it, as we found out three days later.

We were all summoned to a mass briefing, carried out in separate halls across the base at the same time. I guess the same briefing was going on at other camps right across the US.

We all filed in and sat down, and found ourselves looking at a large map on the wall in front of us. I could tell straight away it was one of the Pacific islands, it had that same sharp angled shape that so many of them had. The island of Tinian had looked a bit like that from our Marianas briefing. Plus there were the unmistakable signs of defences marked on it.

Paddy, sitting next to me, gave me a happy wink. This meant action!

"OK, let me have your attention," snapped the briefing officer.

He tapped the map of the island tacked to the wall with his pointer.

"This, gentlemen, is Iwo Jima! Right inside Japanese territorial waters. Eight square miles, and nearly every square inch of it hides an underground Japanese defence position. Those of you who were at the Marianas, this is more of the same. But much more. This mountain here, the highest point on the island, is called Suribachi. It's a dead volcano. Which means the sand on the beaches is the same as you got bogged down on at Saipan, Guam and Tinian. Black volcanic ash."

As I heard this, my heart sank. That black ash is almost impossible to walk through, let alone run through at speed trying to dodge enemy fire. I'd only been in battle for a short while, but I'd learnt that much.

"When I say it's heavily defended, believe me, I'm not joking. The beaches will be mined, have no doubt about that. Our reconnaissance planes have also spotted sections just offshore where oil drums have been tied together and are floating in the surf. Their guess is that they contain explosives to be set off as soon as we reach them.

"Here, here and here, where the beach ends and the island proper begins, are terraces of rock. Some of them are twelve feet high. So we can't just run our tanks up from the beach.

"When you get off the beach you'll find that most of the island is just rock and scrub. Very little vegetation for cover.

"This assault means getting across the soft sand, then climbing up these rocks, and aiming for here..." And he tapped the outlines of the airfields. "Two fully-operational airfields and a third under construction. And those airfields, gentlemen, is why we have to take Iwo Jima."

I sat there with a sense of awe at what we were expected to do. And already, a sense of fear deep in my stomach. It was going to be like Saipan all over again, only worse.

The briefing officer continued:

"If we're going to win this war, we have to bomb Tokyo into submission. The problem is our nearest air base is the Marianas, some fifteen hundred miles from Japan. And I don't need to tell you that a three thousand mile round trip is too far for our fighter planes. So our B-29s have been flying their bombing missions to Japan without fighter escort, and they've been hitting major interception from enemy fighter planes based here at Iwo. The fact is, our bombers have been sitting ducks.

"Further, if any of our planes get into trouble, there is nowhere safe for them to come down. If they don't make it back to base they have to ditch in the sea. That often means the loss of both the plane and the crew."

"See, John," Paddy whispered to me. "I told you this was going to be the Big One!"

I could sense his excitement at going to fight this battle. It was what Paddy enjoyed: danger. For me, once again – as I had felt before we landed at Saipan – I just felt a hollow feeling in the pit of my stomach. Before Saipan there had just been fear of what battle would be like. Now I'd experienced it, and been injured – and it had been every bit as bad as I thought it would be.

The officer was talking again, and I did my best to let him have my undivided attention.

"Iwo Jima is the ace card in this Pacific War," he said firmly. "Whoever holds it, wins. If we take this island, we can bomb Japan into submission. So long as the Japs hang on to it, we can't. In other words, we *have* to take Iwo Jima.

"That's the good news. The bad news is the Japanese have had a very long time to make this island a fortress. Those of you who were in the Marianas saw what the Japs had done there. Tunnels. Caves. Everything deep underground. We bombed them and bombed them before the attack, but they were still there, alive and kicking. We're going to do the same to Iwo, but on an even bigger scale and hope this time we can really knock them out. But our experience suggests we can't count on it being one hundred per cent successful. If that's the way it's going to be, OK, we'll take any percentage we can.

"We don't know how many Japanese troops are on the island. Intelligence suggests there could be anything between twenty and forty thousand of them."

"Wow!" whispered Paddy next to me, getting even more pleased as the obstacles in the way of this operation mounted up. I hoped he never found out how my sense of fear was growing the more I heard.

"I'm not going to pretend this is going to be easy," continued the briefing officer.

You can say that again, I thought.

"You'll be up against some of the fiercest defensive fighters in the world. As we've seen already, these soldiers would rather die than surrender. They're bunkered deep inside into one of the most impregnable defensive structures ever constructed. But we have to take Iwo Jima, and if there are any men on this earth who can take it, then it's you. Because you're United States Marines."

Jimmy Wilson

So it was that Christmas Day 1944 found me, along with many thousand other Marines, loading out. Fifteen days later we were aboard troop carriers, battleships, and a whole fleet bound for Iwo Jima.

The sea journey was a long one. Forty days. Forty days to do nothing except talk and read and talk and sleep and argue and complain. Just like all soldiers all over the world, we complained about everything there was to complain about. The food. The ship. The sea. The officers. The enemy. It didn't do us any good, but it helped pass the time.

There were a lot of new recruits among our unit on that voyage out. One of them, a fellow the same age as myself, but who seemed to me to be a lot younger, named Jimmy Wilson attached himself to me and Paddy on the voyage. He was from New Jersey, and I can't think what on earth made him enlist in the Marines. Maybe he thought it would make him look big back home. Right now, on the way to Iwo, he just seemed scared all the time. It was all he wanted to talk about.

Personally I tried not to encourage him. I knew all about fear. I'd felt it on Saipan. I was certainly feeling it now. But talking about it didn't make me feel any better. Also, it might give the other guys the idea you were some kind of coward, and that was the last thing you wanted people to think of you. Especially when you were going into combat.

I tried to tell him this one afternoon, when just he and I were standing on the deck of our ship, looking out over the vast empty sea. Jimmy had just finished telling me how nervous he felt about actually facing the Japanese guns on the beach.

"Is it really that bad, John?" he asked. "You've been there. You've been shot. You're a hero."

"I'm no more a hero than any other man in his outfit, Jimmy," I said. "I was only on Saipan for a short while. I only got as far as the beach, and then up to the pillbox where the sniper was hiding who shot me."

I looked at him, and felt such deep sympathy for him as I saw the look of deep worry on his face. Deep down I knew I was as scared as he was. He was looking to me for some words that would make him feel better. I knew, no matter how scared I felt myself, I had to say something to try and help him. Some sort of advice.

"Listen, when you go up that beach you don't think about being a hero," I told him. "Hell, you don't even think about the Japanese guns. All you think about is staying alive. And maybe getting to where you're supposed to get to.

Because if you stay stuck, you're dead. If you try and go back, you're dead. So the only way to stay alive is going forward, keeping your head down and look every which way."

"But I don't know if I'll be able to kill a Japanese soldier if I saw one face to face," he continued, his face creased into a look of pain.

"Believe me, you'll do it," I assured him. "One, there ain't time to think in battle. Two, if you don't kill him he's gonna kill you. That makes it very simple." I then added, trying not to hurt his feelings too much, "And a word of caution, Jimmy. Me, I don't mind you opening up to me this way. About your feelings, and everything. But some of the other guys might not take it that way."

"I know," nodded Jimmy, and he dropped his eyes unhappily. "I said this back in boot camp and I got called a coward. I had to fight to prove I wasn't."

"Well you don't have to fight me," I reassured him. "But take my tip, keep your mouth shut. Believe me, to hear someone else saying they might be scared, it doesn't do the other guys any good. Trust me, we're all scared. But if we start admitting it out loud, we might as well all pack up and go home. And remember, the enemy are as scared as we are."

"Are they?" asked Jimmy. "I hear their soldiers kill themselves rather than surrender. That don't sound to me like they're scared of dying."

I was about to reluctantly tell him that I agreed with him, when I was saved from saying anything by the sound of a siren sounding throughout the ship. This was followed by a terse announcement over the ship's loudspeakers: "Enemy attack! Enemy attack! All hands to battle stations!"

Kamikaze

As Marines on board a naval vessel, we weren't scheduled to take part in the ship's defensive operations. While the sailors ran to their positions, Jimmy and I looked out over the sea. A number of small planes were coming at us. Not just at us, but at the whole fleet.

The shipboard anti-aircraft guns opened up with their ear-splitting chatter chatter chatter, peppering lines of tracer towards the incoming Japanese fighter planes.

I could make them out better now as they got nearer. Five Japanese Zero planes. Single-seater fighter bombers. Gunfire came from the planes and Jimmy and I threw ourselves down as the bullets strafed the side of our ship. Once again I was under fire and my heart began thumping loudly. I did my best to get it under control, taking deep breaths, trying to keep calm. The worst thing I could do was to show my fear in front of Jimmy.

I heard the plane zoom past. I stood up again, hauling Jimmy up with me. The deep breathing had worked. My heart had returned to almost normal. Jimmy was shaking.

"It's OK," I assured him. "Our boys have got them in their sights."

To prove my words, one of the planes burst into flames in mid-air as our anti-aircraft gunfire hit home. There was the flash of an explosion, and then it spiralled down into the sea.

"One to us," I murmured.

The other Japanese Zeros were whirling through the sky, guns blazing. And then, as we watched, one of the planes banked and set a straight course directly for one of our ships. Unflinchingly, the plane kept on its direct flight path. The anti-aircraft guns opened up, and I imagined that on board they were desperately trying to aim a rocket at the oncoming plane, but before they could do so the Japanese plane smashed into the ship's tower. There was an almighty explosion as the plane's bomb load blew up, and then the ship was ablaze.

We watched in horror as the ship became an inferno of fire, more exploding ammunition adding to the carnage.

Further out, through the smoke of the burning ship, I could make out another of the small planes making a direct line straight for another of our fleet. This time the gunners brought it down, but only just in time. The small plane spun out of control, its wings shot off, and crashed into the sea just by the ship.

The remaining two Japanese planes were shot out of the sky by a mixture of rockets and intensive anti-aircraft fire. They could have taken evasive action, but it looked obvious to me that both planes had been on a collision course at their intended targets. Because they'd been flying so straight, so low, our guys had been able to pick them off.

Meanwhile, one of our ships was still burning. From this distance I could see the crew and Marines scrambling and jumping down the side of the burning ship into the sea. Lifeboats were being lowered.

Our own course had already been altered to head for the burning ship, to pick up survivors.

Jimmy looked at me, his face white, his lips trembling.

"They crashed on purpose!" he said. "They flew their planes right into those ships, knowing they were killing themselves at the same time."

I nodded.

"Kamikazes," I said. "Suicide pilots. I'd heard about them, but I've never seen them before."

"What hope have we against men who don't care if they die!" begged Jimmy.

"A lot," I told him firmly. "They die once, that's it, their war is over. The Japanese are scared of us because we don't die. We keep coming at them. That's why we're going to win."

But even as I said it, I knew that my words sounded hollow. This was our enemy. Men for whom death held no fear. These were the soldiers we would be facing when we got to Iwo Jima. This was going to be a battle with few survivors.

Fight

For the next two days after the kamikaze attack on our invasion fleet, the situation on all the boats was tense. We kept expecting the kamikaze planes to come back, and in larger numbers. Especially the nearer we got to Japanese waters.

However, after the third day with no sign of further attacks, things eased off. At least, for most of us. I noticed that Jimmy Wilson still seemed as shaken up as ever. I guessed the Japanese were holding their kamikaze pilots for us for when we arrived at Iwo Jima, along with plenty of other nasty surprises.

Our ship was now packed to the limits – as were all the others in the fleet – with the survivors from the ship that had been hit. With thousands of us packed in tight, and not many places to go to escape one another, I guess it was inevitable that sooner or later trouble would rear its ugly head. It popped up for me in the shape of my pal, Paddy Riley, with a black eye.

"What happened to you?" I asked.

"I had to put some joker right," said Paddy.

"About what?" I asked.

"About you. I overheard him mouthing off about you being a Nazi spy."

I stared at him.

"Not Henry Pelt?!"

"I don't know what his name was, I didn't give him a chance to tell me. He was one of the survivors off the boat that got hit by that kamikaze suicide pilot. Just our luck to have a yo-yo like that transferred to us. I heard him mouthing off about you, so I called him out. Next thing the two of us are going for it." He touched his eye tenderly. "Man, he's tough!"

"What happened?"

"Sergeant Sykes came along, so we broke it up." He added fiercely, "But it ain't finished."

"Yes it is, Paddy," I said.

Briefly I told him about Henry and our background. Our time at school, and Henry's attitude towards me and my family. When I finished, Paddy looked at me, sympathetically.

"Man, that is tough!" he said. "To have an idiot like that on your back all the time."

"He wasn't on my back till his ship sank," I said ruefully. "I guessed he'd be coming out here to Iwo. Hell, nearly every Marine there is, is in this fleet. But I thought he'd just stay with his battalion on his ship and I wouldn't have to see him or talk to him or anything." I sighed. "Looks like I was wrong. I guess now Henry's on our boat, he's going to keep this stupid thing going."

"Trust me, John, he won't keep it going much more," grunted Paddy. "Not when I finish shutting his mouth up. How can any idiot call you a Nazi after what you did on the Marianas?! Hell, I'm Irish, you're German, Luigi there is Italian. We all came from somewhere else."

"I know," I agreed. "But that's because that's what Henry is, an idiot."

"Yeah, well, he's gonna be an idiot with a bloody nose!" snapped Paddy.

I shook my head.

"Leave it, Paddy," I said. "Thanks for standing up for me, but it's OK. I can handle Henry. I handled him all the way through school. And it won't make me feel better if you end up court-martialled for fighting with another Marine."

Reluctantly, Paddy nodded.

"OK, John," he said. "But that Pelt guy sure as hell hadn't better say anything like that again when I'm around!"

As I left Paddy to go and get some treatment for his eye, my heart sank a little. It was bad enough that I was about to go into combat against an enemy who didn't care about dying, on top of that I had my old enemy Henry Pelt to contend with, right here on this ship. I just hoped I wouldn't have to suffer him when we actually got to Iwo Jima.

Iwo Jima

For the next few weeks on board ship I didn't have anything more to do with Henry Pelt. Now and then we saw each other, but – as we had done on the train on our way back to camp from Kalamazoo – we kept our distance and didn't even acknowledge each other. I guessed he was still telling his cronies his mad theories that I was a Nazi spy, but he didn't say it to me to my face. Nor did he say it out loud to too many others, either.

I guess it might have been because he found out there were a lot of other men on board who came from German families, and Pelt was intelligent enough to know that mouthing off that all Germans were Nazis would have got him into the same sort of trouble he'd got into with Paddy Riley.

I had to admit, seeing him and thinking about what he said made me feel a bit strange about being German. I think all of us who still had family in Germany felt that way a bit. How were our cousins and aunts and uncles feeling about us right now? At least for those of us who were out in the Pacific fighting the Japanese it wasn't so bad. I wondered how the guys fighting in Europe felt. Especially the crews of the planes who were dropping bombs on their own relatives at Dresden and Munich and Berlin.

Still, that's war. You have to fight for what you believe in.

The days went past and turned into weeks. Every day brought us nearer to Iwo Jima. Every day I did my best not to think about what was waiting for us when we got there. Most of the other guys did the same, which is why the ship was full of guys playing cards, reading, doing loads of different things, but avoiding talking about the impending battle if they could.

Finally we were there. Iwo Jima.

We heard the sounds of battle long before we saw the island.

Our briefing officer back at camp had told us that they were intending to soften up Iwo with a major bombing campaign. Well, he was as true as his word.

The non-stop bombing of Iwo Jima by our Air Force had been going on for over two months. The longest and heaviest bombardment there'd ever been in the Pacific. Now we were here, with our heavy battleships to add to that bombing. Iwo Jima was being pounded into rubble.

As I stood on the deck and looked towards Iwo, about two miles away, I was reminded of when we were waiting to attack Saipan. Saipan had been bombed too. Not as heavily as this, but it had been bombed. And the enemy had survived.

Iwo Jima seemed to be permanently on fire. The island's one mountainous peak, Suribachi, was shrouded in smoke as missile after missile from our battleships and cruisers hit the island.

"No one can possibly stay alive under all that bombing," said a voice beside me.

It was Jimmy Wilson, looking out towards the island with a stunned expression as more bombs and rockets rained down on the island.

I decided it was time for more straight talking to him. It was wrong to send him into battle thinking it was already won. If that happened, he was as good as dead.

"Our battleships did the same thing when we invaded Saipan," I told him. "They bombed the island until we didn't think there could be anything or anyone left. But when we hit the beach, the Japs were waiting for us."

"But they say our guys have been bombing Iwo every day for over two months!" insisted Jimmy, and I could hear the note of desperate hope in his voice. He didn't want to go on to that beach and face a live enemy shooting at him. None of us did.

As I looked at the beach on Iwo, again I remembered Saipan. The defensive fire we'd encountered. The dead Marines strewn about around me on the beach as I dug into the sand. And the final shot that tore my chest open.

I could feel myself sweating beneath my uniform. The fear was creeping up on me again. I hoped Jimmy hadn't noticed.

"Remember the kamikaze pilots?" I reminded him. "Fight to the death. Commit suicide rather than surrender. And take your enemy with you as you die, if you can."

More rockets blasted into the island. More explosions and flames. The sea around us boiled with the recoil. It was like watching an island being blown up by an earthquake or a volcano. Only this volcano was man-made by sixteen-inch guns of our battleships and the fourteen-inch guns of the destroyers and cruisers.

"They're not answering our fire. They must surely all be dead!" Jimmy continued.

As he spoke, there was a movement from the base of the cliffs on the island as the large Japanese guns moved in their casements, and then smoke from their muzzles and the sound of thunder rolling to us across the sea.

"Down!!" came the shout, and we all ducked down.

The next second I felt our ship rock and there was the deafening sound of a blast off our port bow.

I lifted my head and peered over the rail. The Japanese had scored a direct hit on one of our gunboats. It was on fire. As I watched I could see men leaping from it into the water. From this distance they looked like toys.

Jimmy got to his feet and looked, too, and his face was white.

"For dead men, those Japs sure as hell can fight back," I said bitterly.

Another round was fired from the island, and this one finished the gunboat off altogether, toppling it over. Still on fire, it began to sink down, and then lay, half-in half-out of the water, caught on the offshore waters.

"All men below decks!" came the barked orders from one of the Sergeants.

I turned and headed for the hatch. Jimmy Wilson stood, still staring at the men in the water and the burning ship as if transfixed, a look of horror on his face.

"Watching won't help them," I said, maybe a bit too sharply. Jimmy turned and looked at me, his lips trembling.

"We're going to die," he said, the terror apparent on his face.

I took a deep breath. For his sake, and for mine, I had to keep my fear under control.

"Not necessarily," I told him, doing my best not to let my voice shake. "When the time comes, just keep your head down and follow orders. Come on, let's get below."

As dawn came up the next morning, it hit me that this was it. D-Day.

The sea was calm. No wind. The sky was clear of cloud. Visibility was excellent. The Japanese would be able to see us coming clearly all the way in, the whole two miles. The question was, would they try to hit us while we were still out at sea, or would they wait until we got on to the beach, when we'd be closer targets.

Breakfast had been the standard before an assault: a great helping of steak and eggs. It was a standing joke amongst the Marines. "The condemned man ate a hearty meal." The sick feeling in my stomach meant I'd had difficulty eating. I noticed that Jimmy Wilson didn't touch his food at all.

0900 had been set as the time for the assault. H-hour. We assembled on deck and I took in the scene. Our gunships were sending rockets into the beaches, doing their final best to clear them ready for our landing. Marine and Navy planes were also at work attacking the island, hitting the areas beyond the beaches.

There was a flurry of activity on our ship, and on all the landing ships along the line. Landing craft were being lowered from the assault transports, boat teams were being assembled, amphibious tractors being unloaded.

"OK, Platoon! Over the side and into the boats!"

"Back in action again, John!" Paddy grinned at me. "Watch you don't get shot again. The army can't afford to keep giving out Purple Hearts!"

I forced a grin back at him, though inside my heart was pounding and my throat felt tight. Fear, which had to be shut out.

Along with the others, I moved towards the nets that hung down from the side of the ship and led to the waiting landing boat. I noticed Jimmy Wilson hang back, and I went over to him.

"I don't want to die, John," he whispered as he saw me approach.

"None of us do, son," said a gruff voice behind me.

I turned, surprised, and found Sergeant Sykes just behind me.

"Trouble?" Sykes asked me.

I shook my head.

"No, sir," I answered.

"Good," said Sykes.

But I could tell he didn't believe me. One look at Jimmy, trembling, was enough for him to know what was going on. I expected him to bawl Jimmy out, order him to the boats. But to my surprise, Sykes turned to Jimmy and spoke gently to him.

"You're scared, kid," he said. "We're all scared. I'm scared. Any man with a brain in his head is going to be scared, doing what we're about to do. Except for guys like Paddy Riley. They seem to get a kick out of being in dangerous spots."

I looked at Sykes in surprise. This was the last thing I'd have expected, to hear him, of all people, admit that he was scared.

"It's being scared that's kept me alive," Sykes carried on. "I know when to duck and hide. Dead men are no use to this army. But if we don't get out there and win this war, then we're gonna have a great deal more to be scared about. Our families and our children, and our grandchildren, living in a world ruled by people like Hitler and the Japanese commanders. We can't let that happen."

With that Sykes clapped Jimmy on the shoulder.

"Remember what I said," he said. "Keep your head down and follow orders. You'll be OK."

With that he moved to the rail where the rest of our platoon was clambering over and into the nets down to the landing craft.

I looked after him, astonished. Sergeant Sykes admitting he was scared?! He was one of the bravest soldiers I'd ever known.

It was ironic, what Sykes had said had been for Jimmy's benefit, but in those few words he had made me feel that if Sykes could cope with his fear, then so could I.

"Come on, Jimmy," I said. "Let's go. Like Sykes says, we've got a war to win."

I headed for the rail where Paddy was waiting for me. Jimmy followed me.

"Come on, John!" Paddy called cheerfully. "We don't want to miss this one!"

Again I thought of what Sykes had said about people like Paddy. The people who get their fun looking for danger. I wondered if anything ever scared Paddy?

We climbed over the side of the ship and down the net into the boat and joined the rest of our platoon. The small landing vehicle rocked from side to side in the sea.

This was it. We were on our way to face the enemy.

Landing

Rockets and missiles from our battleships still pounded the island, the barrage continuing non-stop. Luckily the sea was calm, so our landing craft boat didn't rock too much. I could see the reconnaissance planes flying over Iwo, radioing the positions of the Japanese defences back to the battleships to help them pinpoint their targets.

As I watched, the large battleships moved in closer to the island, trying to get as close to their targets as they could so they could knock out the pillboxes and blockhouses.

"That sure is some fancy shooting!" muttered one Marine near me admiringly as shell after shell from the *Arkansas* smashed into the Japanese defences. "Hope they leave something standing for me to take. I promised to win me a medal to take home for my pa."

"OK, men!" hollered Sgt Sykes. "We're go!"

Our assault craft moved away from our mother ship. Ahead of us were a wave of amphibian tractors armed with 75 mm howitzers and machine guns. Their job was to try and clear a path for us on to the beach by keeping up a steady fire at everything in their way. The theory was that the armed tractor would haul on right up on to the beach and we'd just follow it up.

After us would come the LSMs bringing the tanks and bulldozers. Then, once the Marines were on shore and moving in, the final section of this first wave would land, the corpsmen and Seabees.

I knew in my gut that it was going to be Saipan all over again. It was going to be hard, bloody and messy.

However, so far there had been no firing from the island. No defensive rockets, no small arms fire. Nothing. The enemy were waiting and holding their fire.

We all crouched down in our landing craft, keeping our heads down. My guts felt like they were twisted and I could feel the sweat on my hands as I gripped my rifle.

I thought about what Sergeant Sykes had said. He was scared. I was scared. We all were scared. Except Paddy Riley.

I turned and looked at Paddy, who was crouched next to me.

Paddy gave me a wink. This was what he loved. Action!

I forced a wink back at him.

Then I turned and looked at Jimmy Wilson, crouching down on the other side. His face was whiter than ever and his lips moved as if in silent prayer. He didn't look at me, he didn't look at anyone or anything. He was just absolutely terrified.

"It'll be OK," I whispered encouragingly to him. But he didn't respond. For one thing, the noise of the bombing and the sea and the engine of our craft meant my words were lost. But the main thing was, he was lost inside himself in fear.

As we neared the beaches there was a roaring noise from overhead. I looked up. There above us in the sky were a force of B-29 bombers, heading for Iwo. As we watched they began their bombing of the island, bombs raining down and filling the morning sky with smoke and explosions. Following the B-29s came the dive bombers, once again pinpointing pillboxes and blockhouses.

By now we were almost at the shore. The waves broke over our landing craft. Ahead of our troop-carriers the armoured amphtracs had reached the beach and begun climbing out of the surf on to the black volcanic sand of the beach. Still there had been no fire from the Japanese positions.

"Maybe they're all dead," murmured someone.

"Don't bet your life on it," replied someone else.

It was as our landing craft rode in on the surf towards the beach that the Japanese defences opened up with mortar and artillery shells. The water around our craft shot up in columns as mortars crashed around us. On our starboard side one of our craft took a direct hit. The two dozen men in it tumbled into the water. Some of them were already dead and just sank. Others, injured, did their best to keep afloat, but the weight of their full packs pulled them down beneath the surface of the water.

I turned my eyes away from the scene and concentrated on the beach that was fast approaching. More explosions around us. More columns of water crashing down on us.

Our craft lurched slightly as the caterpillar tracks bit into the loose sand beneath the waves. Then we were coming up out of the surf, trundling on to land. We'd made it. We were on Iwo Jima.

On the Beach

"Keep your heads down!" shouted Sykes.

Those of us who'd done this sort of thing before didn't need to be told, we were already crouched, heads down. This was where many a novice met his end, peering up at the beach from over the rim of the craft and giving a sniper a good target.

Now that we'd made land, the Japanese defences opened up with a vengeance. Mortars and artillery fire rained down on us, bullets ricocheting off our armoured landing craft.

"OK!" shouted Sykes, raising his voice so he could be heard above the sounds of gunfire. "Let's get off this thing! Hit the beach!"

The landing ramp crashed down on the black volcanic sand, and keeping low we broke into a stampede for the nearest raised ridge of sand. I threw myself down face first into the soft sand. Paddy was next to me. Bullets whizzed over our heads, still clanging off the armour of the landing craft.

I rolled over and looked behind me, searching for Jimmy Wilson. He was still crouched in the amphtrac, his face petrified.

"Get outa there, Marine!" bellowed Sykes. "Get outa there before they kill you!"

Jimmy forced himself up, and then began to run forward, his boots clanging on the metal of the landing ramp. As he reached the sand he suddenly stopped as if he'd been hit by a truck. He spun round, and then crumpled. Even from where I was lying I could see the blood on the pale skin of his neck.

I felt sick. I also felt to blame in some way. I knew how scared he was. I was scared, but I was doing my best to control it. Jimmy couldn't.

Maybe I should have told him to go to the company doctor. Pretend to be sick. But no, I knew that wouldn't have worked. The doc would have just given him some pills and kicked him out. And if Jimmy had told the truth, that he was too scared to go into combat, then he would have been thrown in the brig, and then sent back in disgrace. Would he have been able to stand that? I didn't know.

Suddenly all Sykes's words of advice to Jimmy seemed hollow. Jimmy had followed orders, he'd gone into battle, and Jimmy had been shot.

Then it hit me – no, I was wrong. Jimmy *hadn't* followed orders. Jimmy had stayed behind on the amphtrac, and so given the enemy sniper time to get a good aim at him. If he'd followed Sykes's orders he would have been up here on the beach with the rest of us right now, in cover behind this ridge.

I saw Jimmy suddenly move, and realized that he hadn't been killed, just wounded, and I felt a little better. Now he would be picked up by the corpsmen and taken back to the boats and tucked away nicely. He could sit the rest of the war out with a Purple Heart, a war hero, wounded at Iwo Jima.

It was an ironic thought. It made me realize that the same thing had happened to me, in a way, back at Saipan. Shot in the first few minutes of the landing. This time on Iwo Jima I'd survived this far. Now I was up against the proper test. Could I go all the way?

Tug Reed, our radio operator, was near to me, calling into his mike, reporting our situation back to the ships.

"Fox Company 28th Division landed on Green Beach safely. Limited casualties, but coming under heavy fire now. Over."

There was a crackling from his radio set as the base responded. I couldn't make out what they were saying – for that you needed a radio operator's ears, trained over years of making out what people were saying through radio hiss and static – but from his reply I guessed they were asking what sort of fire we were coming under.

"Mainly small arms fire. Machine guns," reported Tug.

A huge explosion just ahead of us shook the ground beneath me and sand and rocks rained down on us.

Tug shook the sand off him, spat more sand out, and added into his mike: "Also mortar fire. Over."

I realized that the Japanese had starting using mortars against us because here, behind this ridge, we were also in the cover of the first terrace of rock, which was about three feet high. It didn't give us much protection, but just enough to make it difficult for the machine gunners and snipers to get a bead on us.

Above us I knew there was a pillbox. I'd spotted it as we came in to land. Low, squat, with a narrow opening in its concrete face, half-buried beneath sand and earth for camouflage, somehow it had survived the intensive bombing. I was back in the same situation as I'd been at Saipan, trapped on a beach, held down by gunfire from a concealed pillbox. Back on Saipan I'd tried to knock it out, and had got shot for my pains.

"OK, you guys," said Sykes. "We gotta take that pillbox out else we can't move off this beach. It's no use radioing for rockets from the ships to knock it out. For one thing it's set too low down, and if they haven't knocked it out so far, they're not going to do so now. Also, at this range, our ships are just as likely to hit us."

Almost as if it was someone else's voice speaking, I heard myself say: "I'll do it, Sarge."

It was as if Sykes's words to Jimmy back on the boat had struck some kind of chord in me. I had to know if I could get a handle on my feeling of fear and do what was right. Not just for me, but for the others back home.

"You don't go without me," grunted a voice beside me. It was Paddy.

Sykes looked at me quizzically.

"You sure about this, Smith?" he asked. "Last time you tried this you got badly shot up."

"Maybe this time I get the chance to do it right," I said wryly.

It sounded brave, but deep down I didn't feel it. I still remembered the fear I'd felt when I'd gone up to the pillbox on Saipan. Saw the rifle poking out at me. Looked down into it. I'd be facing that again, but if I didn't, I knew I'd never be able to get past it. It was something I had to do – not just for the platoon, but for myself.

Sykes nodded.

"OK," he said. "Which way will you go up?"

I did my best to remember how the pillbox was sited. If my observation had been correct, it jutted out from an overhang of rock. That was part of its camouflage. I hoped the rock would give me some cover.

"There's a body of rock to the right of it," I said. "If I can get up that way, with luck I might be able to get a couple of grenades through the opening."

"I'll be right behind you, gun ready," said Paddy. "If I see any rifle barrels poking out at you, I'm gonna let them have it, so get ready to dive for the ground when I shout."

"Good," said Sykes. "In that case I'll take some men up towards the left, keep 'em busy with a decoy action." He shouted along the line: "Redmond, di Maggio, Anderson! You're with me!"

With that, Sykes began crawling along the beach, using the ridge of sand and the terrace of rock behind it as cover. Redmond, di Maggio and Anderson followed him, moving jerkily forward on their knees and elbows, guns at the ready.

I looked at Paddy.

"Looks like us again." I forced a grin.

"You sure you're ready for this?" asked Paddy quietly, and I suddenly realized that – despite his own apparent lack of fear – he knew how I felt. He knew that memories of being shot on Saipan were with me.

"I can do this and you can be my cover," he suggested.

I shook my head. "No," I said. "This one's mine. Let's do it."

Pillbox

Paddy and I set off, crawling fast and low, digging in with our knees and elbows into the soft sand, me in front, Paddy close behind. When we reached the point where I guessed the rock overhang began, I stopped. I slung my gun over my shoulder and pulled two grenades out.

I looked back at Paddy, checking he was ready. He nodded. All we could do now was wait for Sykes and his decoy crew to open up. We only had to wait a few moments. There was the sound of gunfire from further along the beach, round towards the left. Then the enemy soldiers in the pillbox opened up, their fire aimed towards the decoys. That was my signal.

I hauled myself up from behind the ridge and rolled at speed over the soft sand towards the terrace of rock. To my left the firing was still continuing, Sykes and the boys making it look as real an attack as possible. Suddenly, now I was in action, the feeling of being scared seemed to vanish. All there was, was activity – my body working, taking over from my brain.

I knelt and popped my head up to peer over the terrace. I could see the pillbox above me in the rock, but I couldn't see any rifle barrels. The concrete was so thick that they could fire from deep within. My hope was that such a thick layer of concrete meant they'd be restricted to firing dead ahead, or side to side, and couldn't swing their guns down at me so easily.

I hauled myself up over the terrace of rock on to firmer ground. The opening of the pillbox was just about fifty feet away. Because the opening was so narrow I couldn't afford to take the chance of throwing the grenades and hoping I'd get them in. If I missed it would give away our position, and both Paddy and I would get gunned down for sure. I had to get close enough to pop them in. I gripped the grenades tightly with one hand, leaving my other hand free. I was going to need that free hand if I was going to make it up the slope.

Here goes nothing! I thought. And then I was scrambling up the rock as fast as I could, my fingers tearing at the thin scrub covering the rock to try to get a handhold. The fire from Sykes and the others carried on, hammering away at the Japanese position, holding their attention, I hoped... Fifty feet, forty feet, thirty, getting closer... Twenty, ten...

As if in a dream, or slow motion, as if everything around me had slowed down, I tore the pin from the first grenade, and then the second. One, two, three ... and I tossed both grenades in through the narrow slit.

Then I let myself fall back down the slope, nearly crashing into Paddy, who was close behind me, rifle at the ready.

There was a muffled BOOM! from above me, and then smoke billowed out from the pillbox.

Paddy and I hit the black sand and both lay there for a second, waiting for gunfire from above, but it never came.

The firing from the other side of the pillbox had also stopped.

I was still wiping smoke from my eyes when Sykes and the boys appeared. Sykes was grinning broadly.

"Well done, Smith!" he smiled. "Our way up is clear, at least as far as that pillbox. Let's get this island taken!"

With the pillbox above us out of action, our platoon could now scramble up to higher ground. We still kept low all the time, keeping to the cover of rocks as much as we could, because we didn't know where the next Japanese hiding place might be.

From our new position I turned and looked back at the beach.

From this distance I could see that Jimmy Wilson had managed to drag himself to cover, and had managed to tie something around his neck, so I guessed – and hoped – his neck wound had just been a flesh one. I was glad for Jimmy that for him the War was over.

Elsewhere along the beach other Marines were coming under heavy fire. Casualties were strewn around. Some hadn't even made it to the beach, some floated in the surf. Others lay where they had fallen, half-covered by sand, or draped over rocks.

I guessed our platoon had been fairly lucky.

The strategy that had been set out to us in briefing on our journey out to Iwo was that each battalion had responsibility for a 500-yard stretch of beach. Our battalion's stretch was on the west beach. Our assignment was to go up from the beach and then sweep round the northern base of Mt Suribachi and seal it from the rest of the island.

The other battalions had their own tasks: the 27th was to move west from their position on Red Beach and follow us, but then break off and head due north up the island. The 23rd on Yellow Beach were the battalion nearest to Airfield One. Their job was to get on to the airfield and take it. Then they were also to head north. The 25th, meanwhile, coming ashore on Blue Beach, would then head inland, linking up with the other battalions on the top of the island and join in the chase due north.

For us Marines, our first job was to establish a beach-head. We had to secure the beach so that the next wave could come in behind us: the LSMs that carried the tanks and bulldozers. After them would come the LCVPs. These were also ramp boats which carried half-tracks, anti-tank guns and jeeps. With them came support personnel to take over the beaches after we'd moved on.

Once they hit the beaches the technical stuff started to be put together: laying the wire matting for truck roads so vehicles could make their way over the soft sand and rocks. The shore radio bases would also be established. Passageways would be made up through the steep banks between the terraces.

All this was the great invasion plan, and in the briefing sessions on board ship it had looked great. But a plan on paper and a combat assault in practice were two different things, as I knew from my short experience at Saipan.

For one thing, the sand here was even more treacherous than it had been in the Marianas. Soft and loose and black, it was difficult enough to even walk in. Looking back down at the beach I could see that the trucks that had managed to get ashore were having trouble. Many of them were bogged down, stuck halfway up their wheel hubs in the soft sand.

Many of the half-tracks and tanks were still down on the beach, unable to get up between the terraces because the ground was so steep. I watched them as they moved backwards and forwards along the beach, looking for a way up, while enemy shells burst around them.

Further out, some of the landing craft were now stuck in the surf, pinned down on the beach by Japanese fire. Men were dropping like flies as they came under the barrage of fire.

Looking down at the chaos and carnage on the beach, I reflected that we were the lucky ones. We'd made it this far. But the enemy was still firmly entrenched in their bunkers. From here on in it was up to us.

Under Fire

For the next hour we just stayed where we were, keeping our heads down, and let the enemy fire over us. Mortars dropped behind us, sending out shrapnel in all directions.

Our ships continued to send rockets and missiles over our heads the other way into the Japanese positions on the island. Grimly I weighed up the possibility that with us in the middle of all this heavy crossfire, our chances of getting off this island alive were pretty slim. However, I did my best to push that thought to the back of my mind. This was no time to let my fear take hold of me. I kept reminding myself of what had happened to Jimmy Wilson when his fear had overcome him.

By late afternoon our platoon had scrambled and clawed its way up the rock face of the terraces. Behind us and below us the fighting on the beach continued. The supply amphtracs struggled out of the sea on to the beach under constant enemy fire, bringing with them medical supplies and ammunition. And more and more men. The ship to shore line was opening up, but slowly, and taking heavy casualties.

On our way up the terrace we came upon another half

dozen Japanese pillboxes and bunkers. Three of them had been flattened by our intensive bombing and were just smashed concrete. The other three were still live.

This time other volunteers took on the job of knocking out the first two, both times with grenades through the slit. The third one was a tougher nut to crack.

The Japanese inside it kept up a constant volley of fire, keeping us down, taking it in turns to keep firing. There was no way we could get near it.

Sergeant Sykes crawled over to Redmond, who had the flamethrower.

"You any good with that thing, Redmond?" he asked.

"I can burn a fly at fifteen feet, Sarge," cracked Redmond.

"Forget cooking insects," snapped Sykes. "You think you can take out that pillbox under fire?"

"Only one way to find out," grinned Redmond.

He crawled along the low ridge of rock that gave us cover from the marksmen in the pillbox. Cautiously he peered over the ridge, then ducked his head down again. He looked over at Sykes and nodded.

"Reckon it's worth a try," he said. "I'll give 'em a burst from behind here, just to keep 'em back. Get ready to start firing if they come out."

Sykes nodded. We cocked our rifles ready.

Redmond lay on his back behind the ridge in an awkward

position, the heavy flamethrower held in his powerful hands aimed over his head in the general direction of the concrete Japanese pillbox.

There was an explosion and a sudden roar, and a belch of flame burst out, filling the air.

Then, without seeming to let go of the flamethrower, Redmond was up on his feet, the long flame roaring away, now covering the narrow slit in the pillbox.

The firing from the pillbox stopped abruptly and I was suddenly aware of two men stumbling out, smoke coming from their uniforms. They turned and aimed their guns at us, but before they could fire a hail of bullets from our platoon cut them down, sending them tumbling to earth.

Redmond switched off the flamethrower.

"OK," ordered Sykes grimly. "On we go."

I closed my eyes for a moment and thought of the flamethrower and shuddered at what a weapon like that could do. But then I forced that thought to the back of my mind. This was war, and war was a dirty business.

We dragged ourselves up over the final ridge, and found we were on a plateau stretching north. About a mile from our position, runways, heavily damaged, now mostly craters in places, marked the plateau. We'd made it to the edge of Airfield One.

Dotted across the airfield were more and more concrete

domes, and mounds of earth with slits beneath them. More and more bunkers and underground defensive positions.

"Right, men," said Sykes, looking up at the sky. "This is where we dig in. Remember, our objective isn't the airfield. Our assignment is Mount Suribachi."

We all looked up at the mountain towering above us. The path to it began about a mile away from our position, and it looked to be even more heavily fortified than the airfield.

Up there were more and more Japanese positions, with the tactical advantage of higher ground.

From all over the island I could hear the sounds of battle as the other Marine battalions met fierce resistance from the Japanese defenders. Even though the ships had stopped firing there was the constant noise of mortars and rockets being launched and exploding, and the never-ending ear-splitting chatter chatter chatter of small arms fire hammering out.

My feelings of fear were now beginning to be replaced with extreme tiredness. I wasn't the only one. A look at the faces of the guys around me showed they all felt as exhausted as I did.

Sykes was right to dig in at this stage. Worn down and battle-weary as we were, to have attempted to mount an assault on the base defences of Mount Suribachi would have been suicidal. With darkness beginning to fall, if we didn't get mowed down by hidden machine guns, we'd break our ankles in the potholes in the rocks.

To make sure we were protected against enemy gunfire, we took out our spades and began to dig foxholes for the night. We piled rocks at the edge of the earth holes to give further protection.

After that all we could do was slide down into our foxholes and try and grab some sleep.

Darkness fell quickly, it always does in the tropics. One minute it's daylight, then there's a funny weird kind of light, and the next minute it's black night. So it was here on Iwo, except it didn't stay dark for long.

That night the air was filled with the lights and sounds of explosions from both sides.

Powerful searchlights from our boats out at sea lit up the sky. They were looking for targets high on Mount Suribachi, still intent on pounding it into submission. Rockets fired from the boats powered over our heads and smashed into the mountain, shaking the ground beneath us.

The boats also sent up star shells. These exploded when they were up in the air and came slowly down on parachutes, giving off a bright yellow light, intended to show up any movement by the Japanese.

What with all the noise and the lights, by the time dawn rose on D-Day plus One on Iwo, most of us hadn't slept a wink. I hoped the Japanese had been kept awake as well; I didn't fancy going up against an enemy who not only knew every nook and cranny of this island, but was more alert than I was.

There came a lull in the noise just as the sun began to rise, and I felt my eyelids drooping. At last, I thought, I'm going to get some sleep.

"OK, you guys," snapped Sykes's voice. "Let's go!"

Pinned Down

In fact we didn't go anywhere straight away. As we rose from our foxholes, ready to move towards the path to Mount Suribachi, a volley of fire opened up from the Japanese positions up the mountain, and it kept coming. Machine guns, mortars, rifles, everything rained down on us.

We slid back down into our foxholes behind the cover of earth and rocks we'd thrown up the night before.

Sykes told Tug Reed to get on the R-T and report our position to the ships and get some rockets blasting the mountain.

"And tell them to start hitting it quick! And remember we're here as well!" snapped Sykes. "We want them bombing the Japanese, not us!"

We had marked our positions with white cloth panels to identify us to our own side, so they wouldn't bomb us in error. But mistakes had been known to happen.

From my position just below the airfield, I could look down on the beach far below and see the result of the first day of our attack.

The beach was a mess. For the whole two miles of its length, junk lay on the black sand, or bobbed about in the surf. I could make it out clearly: packs, blankets, rifles, gas masks, and personal articles just lying there. And the larger wreckage, the shattered and wrecked amphtracs, jeeps, tanks, landing craft, half in half out of the water. Many of the heavy machines that had been brought ashore to make the roadways had been hit and lay there, useless. Worse than useless, because – along with all the other wreckage – they formed a barrier which stopped the incoming vessels from finding a place to land.

Now, with dawn, the evacuation of casualties was taking place.

About 2,000 yards offshore were a bunch of LSTs, obviously doubling as temporary hospital ships. The real hospital ships were further out, with the rest of the fleet. As I watched, corpsmen were at work, loading the wounded on to the amphtracs and ferrying them out to the LSTs, backwards and forwards. And all the time they were under Japanese fire.

A sudden fierce explosion from Mount Suribachi shook the ground around us, then another. Our ships were pounding the Japanese positions, just as Sykes had asked.

"OK!" yelled Sykes. "Go go go!!"

Over the ridge we went, and then at a low crouching run for the next available cover, which was a heap of rocks and boulders just a few yards away.

The shelling from our ships may have given us momentary cover, but not for long. The Japanese deep inside their mountain bunkers opened fire. I saw di Maggio throw up his arms and go down. Then I was diving and rolling, crunching into the scrub ground, ignoring the pain as my body hit small rocks, rolling into the cover of the larger boulders.

We regrouped and took stock. In that run of about fifty yards, we'd lost three men. Di Maggio, Compton and Vidor. Their bodies lay sprawled out on the open scrub, Japanese bullets still picking at them.

Sykes grabbed the R-T microphone from Tug Reed and hollered into it: "Fox Company coming under heavy fire. Pinned down at base of Suribachi. Increase bombardment of Japanese positions so we can get going!"

For the next hour the bombardment from our boats kept up, hammering the enemy positions. It didn't seem to have a lot of effect. Now and then there was a lull in their firing, but then it started up again. I guess the enemy had got used to being bombed this way; they'd endured nearly three months of it, even heavier than this. They weren't going to give up now.

All we could do was crouch and hide. Now and then we'd pop up from behind a rock and take a potshot at the Japanese positions above us, but it was of little use, they were too deeply entrenched.

Tug was now getting radio reports about the situation elsewhere. Apparently across the other side of the airfield the other Companies were having the same problem as we were: deeply entrenched Japanese defences keeping them down with constant fire raking across the open ground.

What was worse was that the Japanese positions high on Suribachi also had a perfect view of the airfield itself. Not just the airfield, but of the whole island. While they kept the mountain stronghold, this invasion wasn't going anywhere.

"There's gotta be some way we can get them outta there!" snarled Paddy.

"Listen up!" called Sykes. "We're just gonna have to do this inch by inch. I'm gonna call for more bombing, real saturation. Air strikes. When it happens we're gonna make for that path over there."

The path he was talking about was the main approach to the mountain. A narrow rocky track, it just was 1,300 yards long, and about 200 yards from our present position. After this approach track came the mountain itself, with a series of tracks criss-crossing and twisting and winding up it.

"Stay off the path itself! It's sure to be mined!" Sykes reminded us. "Get into cover either side of it. The nearer we can get to the mountain, the harder it'll be for the Japs to fire down at us. Remember, they're dug in deep. OK? On my signal, because when the bombing starts you ain't gonna hear me calling, that's for sure."

With that, Sykes gave the thumbs up to Tug Reed, and Reed got on to the R-T, giving our position, and the Japanese positions, and calling for air strikes.

Our bombers arrived swiftly, coming in from the aircraft carriers, dodging the anti-aircraft flak, turning over the northern end of the island, and then zooming back in and letting their cargoes hammer into the mountain.

BOOM!! BOOM!! BOOOM!! BOOOMMM!!

Bomb after bomb smashed into the mountain, sending clouds of dust and smoke covering it, as if the old extinct volcano had come alive again.

Amidst the noise and smoke, I looked towards Sykes, and saw him leap out from behind cover and wave his arm, pointing at where the mountain path was.

This was it. Our only chance. I hurled myself out from behind the large rock, rifle at the ready.

We ran, crouching low, as always, as fast as we could, dodging and weaving in case there was a sniper out there, trying to get a bead on us. There was an explosion near me and I half-turned, in time to see Redmond being hurled into the air. He'd trodden on a landmine.

I turned and rushed over to him as he lay, flopped on the earth. He was bleeding badly.

"Stupid!" he muttered, his voice muffled with blood. And then he went limp. He was dead.

Mount Suribachi

I looked ahead. Sykes, Paddy and the rest of the platoon had found cover of a sort in a mixture of rocks and bushes, not far from the narrow path that led to the mountain.

I picked the flamethrower off the ground and hurried over to join the rest of the platoon.

"Redmond's dead," I reported. "Landmine."

Sykes nodded.

"No more rushing," he said. "Before you move, keep your eyes peeled."

He looked at the base of the mountain through his field glasses, studying it.

While he did this, I turned and looked back the way we had come, and across at the airfield.

Our reserves were now moving up to join us, despite the constant fire from the Japanese positions.

By now it was the middle of the afternoon. All these hours had passed and we'd covered just a few hundred yards. During that time the Marines had been launching a steady attack on the airfield itself. Tanks had made it up from the beach and were now advancing across the flat plateau, Marines following in crouching formation behind.

Despite attacks from the Japanese positions higher up the mountain, the Marines on the airfield were doing a good job, clearing out the pillboxes and bunkers.

Sykes put down his field glasses.

"OK," he said, "I've got the picture. There are caves at the foot of the mountain, just near where that path ends. We know the Japanese have been digging tunnels. My guess is they've used existing tunnels inside the mountain to link up from bunker to bunker and pillbox to pillbox. If we can't flush 'em out from outside, we've got to go in and flush 'em out from inside."

What Sykes said made sense. Mount Suribachi was an extinct volcano, riddled with caverns through which lava had run. The Japanese had been on Iwo for years. It was perfect defensive strategy to expand those caverns into a network of tunnels. That was obviously how they'd been able to withstand our bombardment so long, day after day, night after night, by living deep underground. When one bunker came under heavy attack, they just moved through the tunnels to another, like ants working their way through an anthill.

"OK," said Sykes. "There's no way we can get up that path in daylight or we'll all be dead. What we're gonna do is sit tight here, and when it gets dark, which will be in a few hours, we go across the path and make for the caves.

Once in the caves, we split up into pairs and work our way up. Clear?"

We nodded. But once again I could feel the fear rising up in me. We were going into unknown territory. Into caves inside the mountain, where we'd be meeting the enemy face to face. Hand to hand. Fighting to the death.

"OK," said Sykes. "Bunker down. Grab some shut-eye if you can. You're gonna need it. Smith, you and Riley take first watch."

I was relieved to take first watch. The images of what was waiting for us inside those caves would have kept me from sleeping anyway, no matter how tired I was.

So we settled down to wait for nightfall. It came soon enough. And with it came the rain.

After the tropical heat of the day, we hadn't expected it. And it didn't just rain, it poured down, so thick you could hardly see through it. It was like a curtain of water falling down. And it was cold. The previous night had been cold, too, but this was worse. Anyone who thinks a night on a Pacific Island is going to be Paradise ought to spend it outside in freezing rain in a foxhole rapidly turning to mud.

4 a.m. found us armed and ready to move and soaking wet.

"This is worse than when I went to see Grammy's home in Ireland," grunted Paddy. "And believe me, you think it rains in Kalamazoo, that ain't nothing to the rain in Ireland."

"I guess that's why they call it the Emerald Isle," I commented. "All that rain makes the grass grow so green."

"You better believe it," said Paddy. "But at least Irish rain is warm. They call it 'soft'. This stuff is wet and it's freezing and it's hard. I don't envy the Japanese who've been living on this rock."

"They're lucky, they've been living underground," I pointed out.

The foxhole where we were lying was now a small pond. The sides were wet, slippery mud.

"OK!" called Sykes. "Get ready to move out! Keep low, keep slow, keep quiet. And thank God for this rain, it'll give us extra cover."

"It'll give me pneumonia," Paddy complained. "All this way, battle after battle, and I'll finally die of pneumonia."

Under cover of the darkness and the rain we moved forward, slowly, watching for the glint of metal through the wet grass that might be the tell-tale sign of a landmine.

From above us came the sound of firing from the Japanese, but their shots went wide or over our heads. They were firing blind in the dark and the rain, just trying to keep us down.

We stuck to the two sides of the narrow path, keeping

to where it was rocky and therefore not so easy to dig in a landmine.

As we moved, through the rain I saw the tell-tale signs of mines, some of them partly covered, on the path itself. If we'd gone for a full-scale assault along that path, we'd all have been blown to pieces, like Redmond. Again, I felt a tightness on my chest and a sick feeling in my stomach. One false step on one of those, and Booom!! That would be the end.

I took more deep breaths and forced myself to think of other things. Positive thoughts. We were going to win this war. But all the time I kept my eyes peeled, scouring the ground in front of me each time before I put my foot down.

Every now and then the sky would light up as our ships launched more star shells, and we'd throw ourselves down, out of sight of the Japanese. Then we'd stumble up and carry on, getting nearer yard by yard to the foot of the old volcano and the heart of the Japanese defences.

At last we made it.

We staggered out of the drenching rain into the cover of the first cave we came to.

It was great to be out of the rain, but it felt weird to be inside the mountain, inside the Japanese defences.

It suddenly occurred to me that if our own ships and planes carried on bombing Mount Suribachi, now we were in it we could be casualties of our own bombing. Then I remembered that the Japanese had survived this long by staying underground.

"OK," said Sykes. "Let's see what we've got here."

He took out his torch and shone it around the walls of the cave.

Here, in this outer cave, was just rock. But we could see dark patches in the torchlight where tunnels extended deeper into the mountain. "OK," whispered Sykes. "This is where we split up. Two to a tunnel." He gestured at us, splitting us into pairs. Paddy and I, as so often, were paired off.

Sykes took a look at Redmond's flamethrower I was now holding.

"Seeing as you've got it, you might as well keep it," he said.

"No problem, Sarge," I nodded.

"OK," he said. "Let's hit them from where they ain't expecting it. Let's go!"

Inside the Volcano

Paddy and I crept forward into our assigned tunnel. I went first, the flamethrower a dead weight on my arms, and the pack with the gasoline an even heavier weight on my back.

Once we'd left the small entrance cave, I couldn't but be impressed at the engineering feat the Japanese had carried out here. Once the tunnels widened out we saw that this whole mountain was riddled with a maze of passageways, some going off into caves used for storage.

Along the walls ran electricity supply cables, pipes for running water, even pipes that ran hot. I guessed they contained steam to keep them warm below ground.

"Man!" whispered Paddy behind me. "They got a whole city inside here!"

We moved carefully, straining our ears for any sounds of movement ahead.

Above us, further along the tunnels and higher up the mountain, we suddenly heard the familiar chatter chatter chatter of machine gun fire start up. Outside, dawn must have broken, and the Japanese had begun their deadly fire raking the open ground of the airfield, and the path that led to the foot of the mountain.

We set off, heading towards the sound of gunfire. I cradled the flamethrower ready, finger on the trigger, barrel poised pointing straight ahead.

A faint light ahead stopped us in our tracks. Then we edged forward.

A side passage had been cut from this main passageway. It led into a large cave which had been further hollowed out. We were amazed to recognize that this was a hospital, complete with beds, surgical instruments, medical equipment, all deep underground. No wonder the Japanese had survived for so long, despite the attacks.

There was a sound from the entrance to the hospital cave, and we turned round and came face to face with a Japanese soldier. He gaped at us, astonished to find us there. And then his hand reached for the pistol in his belt.

Paddy let off a burst from his rifle that took the Japanese in the chest before he could get his pistol out.

As the dead soldier slumped to the ground, we moved quickly back out into the main passageway. The shots from Paddy's rifle had echoed loudly in the rocks of the caves. My hope was that, with all the firing going on elsewhere, the Japs wouldn't have thought anything unusual was happening.

We hurried along the rock passageway, and now the sound of firing was getting louder. A pillbox was just ahead of us.

I motioned Paddy to stay back. Then I stepped forward into the entrance to the pillbox, the flamethrower poised. I just had time to see the backs of the Japanese snipers, and one turning towards me, surprise on his face, then I pressed the trigger, turning the muzzle of the flamethrower through an arc as I did so.

The flames filled the pillbox. Then it was over. One less Japanese defensive position.

On we went, further on, climbing up, all the time upwards, inside that extinct volcano.

I was soaked in sweat. It wasn't just the weight of the flamethrower, it was the fear that was with me, just beneath the surface. I fought it off. If I let the fear take me over it would make me run. I had to go on. We had to take this island.

Another small passageway appeared just head of us, with more deafening firing. Another pillbox.

I was moving forward towards the entrance, when a Japanese soldier came out. He didn't hesitate, an automatic reaction brought his rifle up and he fired. I felt the bullets pass by me and thud into Paddy just behind me. Paddy yelled and I heard him crash to the rocky floor. I didn't look round, my finger was already pressing the trigger of the flamethrower. The Japanese disappeared in a huge burst of flame.

Wasting no more time, I raced round the corner into the entrance of the pillbox, just as the remaining Japanese soldier was turning to face me, his gun at the ready.

Another roar of belching flame from the flamethrower, and he was finished.

I returned back to the passageway and checked on Paddy. He was alive but the bullets had almost torn his left arm off. Blood was pumping out from between his shattered bones.

"I'll go get help," I told him.

Paddy forced a grin.

"Where from?" he asked, fighting back the pain. "No, go on and finish the job. I've got my right arm. I can hold a gun. I've still got my legs. I'll see if I can make it back to that hospital cave, fix myself up."

"With one arm?!" I said. "We'll get you back to the hospital cave together. I'll fix you up."

Paddy started to protest, but I shut him up. We both knew that if he stayed here, or tried to fix his arm himself, with his arm torn as badly as it was, he'd likely bleed to death.

I fixed a crude tourniquet around the top of Paddy's shattered left arm, and then we headed back down the tunnels, me taking point, the flamethrower at the ready, Paddy stumbling along behind, holding his shattered left arm with his good hand.

We were in luck. We didn't meet anyone on the way back to the hospital cave.

Once there I set to work. First giving Paddy painkillers to dull the agony, and then strapping and bandaging his arm as best I could.

Even with the painkillers, Paddy was in agony as I worked on his shattered arm.

Luckily for us no Japanese came in while I worked on him. I guessed they were too busy manning their defensive positions.

I'd just finished tying Paddy's arm across his chest and fixing it in position with a bandage, when a sudden explosion shook us and pieces of rock began to fall down from the ceiling of the hospital cave. Dust from the passageway poured into the cave. The roof was collapsing!

Rescue

It felt like the whole mountain was coming down on top of us. We ran and stumbled along the passageways, heading towards what we hoped was the outside. Blinded by dust, and coughing, Paddy and I crashed into the rock walls as we hurried, heading downwards all the time. Fear drove me on to go faster. I was terrified that if I didn't get out I'd be buried here under tons of rocks.

Obviously our fleet had begun pounding the old volcano again, trying to drive the Japanese out, or crush them, and they'd scored a direct hit on the part of the mountain just near where we were, in the hospital cave.

By some miracle, stumbling along as we did like two blind mice, we suddenly felt the breath of cold air on our faces and saw faint light through the dust.

We made for it, and soon we were outside, coughing and coughing, spitting up sand and bits of stone, and taking great lungfuls of air.

The old mountain shook again and again as more missiles smashed into it, and then just as abruptly the pounding stopped. All I had was a ringing in my ears.

Then, through the ringing, I could hear the familiar

sounds of rifles and machine guns and mortar explosions.

Out here, in the open air, the battle for Iwo Jima was still going on. The rain had stopped now.

Paddy and I took cover just back inside the entrance to the cave we'd just stumbled out of. Paddy slumped down and settled himself against a rock, where he could at least lie comfortably.

I took a quick look around, checking the surrounding area. There was no sign of Sergeant Sykes or any of the rest of our platoon. I guessed they were still inside the mountain.

I looked along the narrow path over which we'd come during the night. More Marines had made it to the path and I could see them taking cover behind rocks.

I let off a burst of rifle fire at the path, scattering dirt in the air, and then there was an explosion as I hit one of the hidden landmines.

I stopped firing and looked across at one of the Marines who was hiding under cover. I made out a thumbs up sign from him to say thanks for the warning about the path being mined.

Here, in the cover of the foot of the mountain, I now had a good view over the airfield, and my heart gave a leap. US tanks and bulldozers were now firmly in place on the airfield, forming shelter for more Marines to swarm on. It looked as if the airfield had been taken! We were winning!

One of the Marines across the path was now talking into his R-T, and in response a tank appeared, lumbering its way from the airfield.

The Japanese above us on Suribachi opened fire on the advancing tank, but their bullets bounced off its armour.

Nearer and nearer the tank came, crushing scrub beneath its tracks, and riding over rocks. At last it was at the path. Onward it came, remorseless, its great gun swinging down, pointing along the path. There was a BOOOOOM!!! and an explosion, and then more as the shell from the tank detonated a series of landmines on the path in front of it.

Some of the Marines on the far side of the mountain path ran forward and took up positions behind the tank, crouching low, rifles at the ready.

The tank lumbered forward, slowly, defying the bullets of the Japanese snipers higher up the mountain. The Japanese fire seemed less now. I hoped that our platoon had made an impact on the Japanese defences with our attack from inside the mountain. I wondered what had happened to Sergeant Sykes and the rest of our platoon?

As the tank reached our side of the path, the Sergeant in charge ducked out from behind it and ran across to me and Paddy.

"OK, Marine, what's the story?" he demanded.

"PFC Smith from Fox Company, sir," I responded. "Our

platoon has been inside the mountain, taking out Japanese defensive positions."

The Sergeant looked at Paddy and I.

"Are you all that's left?" he asked.

"Hope not, sir," I answered.

The Sergeant nodded.

"OK," he said. To Paddy, he ordered: "Stay here until the corpsmen arrive." To me, he said, "Smith, you're with us."

And so, once more, it was back into the slow business of working our way up the mountain, taking cover behind rock after rock, digging our way into patches of scrub, keeping low, crawling and running, shooting when we could, and hurling hand grenades at concrete pillbox after concrete pillbox.

For the rest of that day we were kept pinned down by the Japanese. They rolled grenades at us down the mountain, they fired round after round at us, they let fly at us with mortar shells. But now our feeling had changed. According to reports that were coming in, already the other Divisions had taken the airfield and were swarming north across the island, heading towards Airfield Two. As they went they were mopping up, destroying the bunkers and pillboxes, digging out the enemy.

Behind us, more Marines were joining us, making their way up towards the mountain and the airfields. However, the Japanese weren't going to give up easily. As we were crouched in our defensive position, I turned just in time to see a group of three Marines who were making their way up the path caught in an explosion.

When the smoke cleared I saw that two of them were obviously dead, sprawled lifeless on the ground. The third was badly hurt and was trying to drag himself away from the crater the explosion had made. He slumped down as a round hit him in his already shattered leg.

I looked around to see if anyone else was near enough to go to his aid, but we were the nearest unit.

"Sergeant!" I called. And I pointed to the wounded Marine, struggling to get to cover, but pinned down by Japanese fire.

"Give me some covering fire," I called. "I'm gonna try and get that guy into cover."

The Sergeant nodded.

"OK, guys!" he called. "Start firing!"

While the rest of the unit opened up with their rifles, I ran and rolled as fast as I could back down the mountain through the scrub until I reached the wounded Marine.

"OK, buddy, let's get you under cover!" I said.

The Marine looked at me, and through the streaks of blood and dirt that spattered his face I was astonished to find myself looking into the face of Henry Pelt.

"Krupp!" he gasped.

That nearly did it for me. I almost turned and left him right there, but seeing him flopping there so injured and useless, I couldn't do it.

Getting into a crouch position, I grabbed him under the arms and began to haul him towards the cover of a large boulder. He whimpered as I pulled him, his shattered legs leaving a trail of blood behind us.

Once in the cover of the boulder I propped him up. Then I tore a strip off his uniform and tied makeshift tourniquets around his legs, just below the knees.

"There!" I grunted when I'd finished. "You'll be OK if you don't move. Stay here until a corpsmen gets to you. They'll patch you up."

I was just turning to make the run back to my position, when I felt his hand grab me.

"John," he said, and I felt a sense of surprise as he said my name. "I'm sorry."

I turned and looked at him, puzzled.

"For what?" I asked suspiciously.

"For calling you Krupp," he said awkwardly. "It was force of habit." He gave a groan as the pain in his legs kicked in, but he gritted his teeth. "And I'm sorry for the way I treated you when we were growing up. I dunno why I did it. I guess I wanted to get back at you 'cos you were smart and I was dumb." He forced a smile. "In case I don't make it, I wanted to say thanks for this, and I'm sorry for the way I was."

"You'll make it," I said gruffly.

Then I softened. All that anger I had felt for him over the years seemed to vanish as I looked at him, lying there so helpless, and so apologetic.

"You always were a tough one, Henry," I said. "You'll make this."

He nodded, and then held out his hand.

"Shake?" he asked.

I nodded.

"Sure," I said. I took his hand and shook it firmly.

"Gotta go now," I said.

He released my hand with a nod.

"Go get 'em, John," he said. "See you back in Kalamazoo."

I caught the Sergeant's eye to let him know I was coming back. He gave the order and they began covering fire again.

I gave one last grin at Henry, and then began my scramble back up the rocks and scrub. As I did so, the Japanese opened up again with their firing.

This battle was still a long way from over.

Day began to turn into night, and still we hadn't advanced. The only good thing was the sight of Sergeant Sykes and some of our platoon stumbling out from the caves of Suribachi. They were covered in dust and dirt.

Sykes and the other guys dodged the Japanese fire to join us at our position. After reporting to the Commander of the company we were with, Sykes came over to join me.

"You got out, then," he said.

I nodded. "I wondered what had happened to you, Sarge," I said.

"We got caught in a rock fall inside one of the caves," he told me. "Lost some of the men. The rest of us managed to dig our way out." He gave a grim smile. "We managed to take out some of the enemy, though. How did you and Riley get on?"

I told him what had happened, and about Paddy being injured.

Sykes nodded.

"So far we're still alive," he said. "That's what counts."

That night as darkness fell we kept to our dug-out positions, guns trained on the volcano, watching and waiting. How long could this go on for? How long could the Japanese hold out before their nerve cracked?

I hadn't slept properly now for four days. Tiredness was once again taking the place of fear. The order had been passed along the line for those who could, to try and grab some sleep. It was going to be a big day tomorrow. So I took the chance to put my head down and close my eyes.

I hardly seemed to have had them shut for more than a few minutes, when the sounds of yells and shooting jerked me awake. The yelling was at close range, and it was in Japanese! We were being attacked!

Raising the Flag

I jerked myself fully awake and snatched up my rifle, my head still fogged with sleep. We were in the middle of a banzai attack.

They must have crept down the mountain under cover of darkness, coming through the tunnels and out through the caves. Now, armed with bayonets, swords and handguns they were hurling themselves at our positions. Shrieking and yelling they came at us. It was the same attitude as the kamikaze pilots. They were here to die, and to take as many of us with them as they could.

The Marines who'd been on watch had raised the alarm and were already opening fire. We joined in, firing as fast as we could as they came towards us.

Onward through the darkness the Japanese came, shouting and yelling and screaming, swords waving, guns blazing.

The Marine next to me fell down dead, taking a bullet through the head.

I blasted away with my rifle, letting them have it, as did the other Marines alongside me.

Then they were on us, and at this close range my rifle was useless, except as a club.

One Japanese hurled himself at me, the knife in his outstretched hand aimed at my face. I hit him hard with my rifle and he fell to the ground.

Then another threw himself at me and I found myself grabbed by one of his arms around my neck. His other hand held a bayonet and he was pulling it back about to stab it into me. I dropped my rifle and grabbed his hand that held the bayonet and struggled to hold it away from me, while at the same time I attacked him with the rest of my body: kicking him with my boots, using my knees, my one free elbow, even smashing my head into his face. It was like the worst kind of street fight. Only here the stakes were the highest: the loser died.

As I struggled with him I was overtaken by a kind of blind fury. I'd come all this way, I wasn't going to die now at the hands of a Japanese soldier armed with just a bayonet.

Suddenly he went limp, and before I knew what I was doing I'd turned the bayonet and felt it sink into his side.

He dropped to the ground and lay still.

I stood for a second, panting hard, my heart pounding inside my chest as if it was going to burst. Then I turned sharply, the Japanese bayonet now in my fist, crouching, waiting to be attacked again. But the attack was over.

None of us slept for the rest of that night; we were all on edge, waiting for another attack. But none came.

When dawn rose next morning we took stock of the situation. We had lost about twenty men. But lying across the base of Mount Suribachi, and sprawled at different points around our defences, were about two hundred dead Japanese. They'd paid dearly for their last-ditch desperate attack.

In the early morning light we continued our upward assault on the mountain, moving slowly, rock to rock, boulder to boulder, but this time we met little defensive fire. There was just the occasional sniper burst from the Japanese. It was as if the night-time banzai attack had been their last major throw of the dice, and they'd lost.

I became aware of more Marines at other points spreading across Suribachi, also making their slow way up the mountain.

For the next four hours we advanced, slowly but surely, knocking out pillboxes when we found them. Higher and higher we climbed.

I remember I turned at one point and looked down from the mountain across the island.

All over Iwo Jima there were Marines, like ants on an ant-hill. Out at sea there were more and more landing craft still coming in, with more reserves. The island was pitted with bomb-craters, ripped and torn apart. Tanks, bulldozers and other heavy machinery were crawling around. The invasion of Iwo Jima was gathering pace.

Then I turned, and looked back up the mountain, and suddenly I felt a lump in my throat and tears came into my eyes.

There, right up at the top of the mountain, the Stars and Stripes was being put up on a pole.

"We did it!" muttered a voice next to me. "We beat them!"

I turned. It was Sergeant Sykes. And I could see that in his eyes there were tears, too. Tears of pride at the sight of the flag fluttering there, on this island that had been thought of as an indestructible fortress.

I nodded, unable to speak. But my tears were not just for the sight of the flag being raised. They were for the men who'd died to make sure it was flown there. Redmond, di Maggio, Compton, Vidor, and all those thousands of other Marines I'd never known. And for guys like Jimmy Wilson, who hadn't died, but had been traumatized by this nightmare.

And also, my tears were for me. I'd come through the danger, and I'd faced my own fear. I'd survived, and I'd proved myself to be a worthy US Marine.

AUTHOR'S NOTE

Although this book is based on real events, additional action has been introduced for dramatic purposes, and also to show actualities of the Pacific campaign that were not apparent in the assault on Iwo Jima. Particularly this is the case with the kamikaze attack featured in this book. In fact the fleet which attacked the Iwo Jima were not subjected to kamikaze attacks. However Japanese pilots did fly kamikaze suicide missions against the American forces elsewhere and at other times in the Pacific campaign.

Kamikaze pilots aimed their planes at the central elevator on aircraft carriers, and at the central bridge on large warships.

More than 2,000 kamikaze missions were flown against the US fleet at Okinawa. During April 1945 a further 1,400 suicide missions were flown in defence of Japanese home islands. These resulted in Allied losses of 26 ships sunk and 160 damaged.

THE BATTLE FOR IWO JIMA AND AFTER

The battle for Iwo Jima was one of the bloodiest battles in the history of the US Marines.

Although the American flag was raised over Mount Suribachi on February 23rd 1945, it was not until March 16th, after a further three weeks of battle, that Iwo Jima was declared secure.

By the end of the conflict the casualty figures showed that out of a force of nearly 60,000 men, 5,391 US Marines had been killed, with a further 17,400 wounded. 2,500 of those US casualties were on the first day of the landings.

Of the Japanese defence force of 23,000, only 216 were taken alive.

The timetable of the assault on Iwo Jima
1944: November: US Navy bombards Iwo Jima for the first time.

December: US Air Force begins its 72-day bombardment of Iwo Jima. This was the longest and heaviest of the Pacific War.

US Navy/Marine invasion force sets out for Iwo Jima.

1945: February 16: US Navy begins a three-day concentrated bombing of Iwo Jima.

February 17: US frogmen suffer 170 casualties while investigating Iwo Jima's beach defences.

February 19: The 4th and 5th Marine Divisions land on Iwo Jima and gain a foothold.

February 23: Marines raise the US flag on summit of Mt Suribachi.

February 25: The 3rd Marine Division is committed to the battle.

March 4: First B-29 bomber lands on Iwo Jima.

March 16: Iwo Jima is declared secure after 26 days of combat.

March 26: 300 Japanese, the last of the island's defenders, launch an early morning banzai charge against US Marines, and are defeated.

April 7: B-29 bombers fly to Japan from Iwo Jima on a bombing raid, escorted by P-51 fighters.

THE IMPORTANCE OF THE VICTORY AT IWO JIMA

1) Heavy B-29 bomber losses over Japan emphasized the need for fighter escorts. Since the 2,800 mile round trip from US air bases in the Marianas to Japan and back was beyond the range of the fighters, a nearer staging point had to be captured.

2) Iwo Jima, with its completed airbases and its close proximity to Tokyo (660 nautical miles or three hours' flying time) would make an excellent strategic base for Allied bombers.

3) Since Iwo Jima was traditional Japanese territory administered by Tokyo, its conquest would mean a severe psychological blow to the Japanese, as well as a vital strategic outpost denied to them.

4) Iwo Jima was a necessary link to the air defences of the Marianas. To isolate Iwo Jima would not be enough, it had to be captured.